THE
BLUE-WINGED TEAL

FIG. 1. Blue-winged Teal, nuptial plumage
Female *(left)* Male *(right)*

THE BLUE-WINGED TEAL

ITS ECOLOGY and MANAGEMENT

BY
LOGAN J. BENNETT
Associate Biologist
United States Bureau of Biological Survey

COLLEGIATE PRESS, INC.
AMES, IOWA
1938

Reprinted, 1966, 1970

THE IOWA STATE UNIVERSITY PRESS
AMES, IOWA, U.S.A.

International Standard Book Number: 0–8138–0215–6

Printed in the United States of America

PREFACE

Throughout the past century many of the wildlife resources in the United States have gradually diminished. That a great catastrophe was in the making has been apparent to some naturalists, economists, scientists, sportsmen and other broad-minded citizens for several decades. Only recently have the masses of our population become alarmed at the probable extinction of many native species of animals.

At Iowa State College interest in the appreciation, the utilization and the husbandry of wildlife resources was evident from the time the institution was founded in 1858. Foremost among the men who encouraged and taught wildlife conservation at Iowa State College were Charles E. Bessey, Herbert Osborn, William T. Hornaday, F. E. L. Beal, Louis H. Pammel and Joseph E. Guthrie. The foundation built by these men prompted the expansion of the wildlife research program at Iowa State College, July 1, 1932. The primary purposes of this enlarged program was to work out methods for the preservation and increase of the desirable native fauna of Iowa. In reality it was hoped that management practices culminating from the research program would aid in pointing the way toward better land utilization and at the same time benefit the valuable species of wildlife found in the state.

The cooperation between the Iowa Fish and Game Commission, Mr. Jay N. Darling and Iowa State College made possible the inauguration of the expanded program. The program was on a three-year basis under the direction of Dr. Carl J. Drake, Dr. Paul L. Errington and the late Prof. Joseph E. Guthrie. Because of the success attained in the enlarged program it was expanded further July 1, 1935, and at the present is supported by Iowa State College, the Iowa Conservation Commission and the United States Bureau of Biological Survey in cooperation with the American Wildlife Institute.

One of the initial projects in 1932 was an ecological study of the native wild ducks of Iowa. This thesis[1] represents re-

[1] A thesis presented to the Graduate College of Iowa State College in partial fulfillment of the requirements for the degree of Doctor of Philosophy.

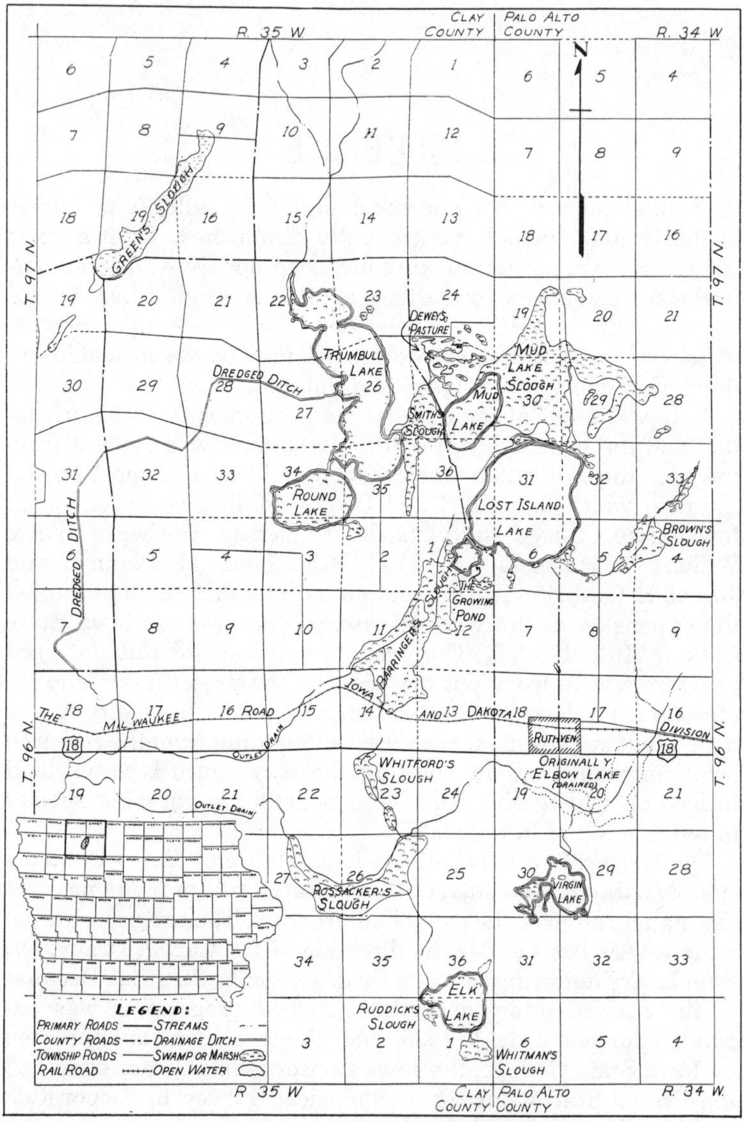

FIG. 2. The Ruthven area, Iowa.

search under this project on the Blue-winged Teal (*Querquedula discors* (Linnaeus)) from July 1, 1932, to February 1, 1937.

The research for the greater part was carried on in northwestern Iowa in Clay and Palo Alto Counties (fig. 2). Those two counties are within the Wisconsin glaciation. With the exception of Lost Island Lake, Elk Lake, Trumbull Lake and Virgin Lake all other water areas in those counties are typical marshes, sloughs or potholes. The region constitutes the largest remnant of duck breeding grounds found in the state. The region is termed "the Ruthven area" throughout this thesis. Supplementary observations were made on the Mississippi River and on other more scattered water areas in Iowa. Mr. Charles Friley, Jr., and the author spent the month of August, 1933, obtaining additional data while on a waterfowl survey through Nebraska, South Dakota, North Dakota, Wyoming, Manitoba, Minnesota and Iowa. The author spent four weeks in Mexico on the wintering grounds during December, 1936, and January, 1937.

It is hoped that the findings presented in this thesis will open the doors of waterfowl management a bit further in order to provide the way for better land use, wise water conservation and the preservation and increase of one of our most important game birds.

ACKNOWLEDGMENT

During the course of this research the author had the excellent advice and counsel of the late Prof. Joseph E. Guthrie, Dr. Carl J. Drake, Dr. Paul L. Errington, Dr. George O. Hendrickson and Dr. E. R. Becker, all of the Department of Zoology and Entomology, Iowa State College. Dr. John Aikman and Dr. Ada Hayden, Botany Department, Iowa State College, contributed much helpful advice to the author in his work. Mr. B. V. Travis, Mr. Gerald Spawn and Mr. F. N. Hamerstrom, Jr., until recently members of the Zoology and Entomology Research Staff, Iowa State College, aided materially in obtaining duck nesting data. Mr. Clarence Sooter, graduate assistant, Iowa State College, made numerous observations for the author during the summer of 1936 that proved to be of great value.

The author takes this opportunity to thank Mr. M. L. Hutton, Mr. Fred Schwob and Mr. Taylor Huston, all of the Iowa Conservation Commission, for their suggestions and encouragement during the course of this work.

The studies could not have been carried out without the hearty cooperation of the citizens of Ruthven, Iowa. Foremost among the Ruthven supporters were Mr. A. L. Bragg, publisher of the Ruthven Free Press, Mr. Lyle Van Vleck, Mr. Tommy Michael, Mr. George Nolan, Mrs. Lydia Knepper Swatosh, and the Ruthven Shooting Club. The Mud Lake Fur Farm members kindly allowed the wildlife research staff to carry on observations on their property near Ruthven.

The wintering ground observations made in Mexico during December, 1936, and January, 1937, could not have been carried on without the invaluable aid of Senor Juan Zinser, chief of Fish and Game, Forestry Department of Mexico, and Senor Daniel Galicia, assistant chief, Forestry Department of Mexico.

The waterfowl reports of the Mexican wintering grounds in 1934 and 1935 by Major E. A. Goldman and L. J. Goldman,

United States Bureau of Biological Survey (unpublished), aided the author greatly in making the wintering ground survey. Particular credit must be given to Mr. C. E. Gillham, United States Bureau of Biological Survey, who accompanied the author in Mexico, for his aid and advice.

Many of the illustrations in this book were taken from negatives furnished by Dr. H. H. Knight, Zoology and Entomology Department, Iowa State College, and by Mr. Herb Schwartz of the Des Moines Register and Tribune, Des Moines, Iowa. Mr. Phillip DuMont kindly furnished negatives for three illustrations. Mr. Sid Horn, wildlife artist, Iowa State College, painted the plate from which the frontispiece was reproduced and sketched the original drawings from which the vignettes were taken for the chapter headings. Maps of the breeding range and flyways were reproduced from McKnight & McKnight Company outline maps by their permission.

My sincere thanks are due to Dr. W. B. Bell and Dr. H. H. T. Jackson of the U. S. Bureau of Biological Survey for checking the manuscript and to Dr. George O. Hendrickson for aiding in reading the proof.

CONTENTS

LIST OF ILLUSTRATIONS

CHAPTER I

Characteristics of the Bird

At the time of the initiation of the waterfowl research in 1932 it was deemed advisable to select for intensive investigation a species of duck that was common enough in Iowa to lend itself to quantitative study. After a survey of the marsh areas in the state it was evident that the Blue-winged Teal (*Querquedula discors* (Linnaeus))[1] was the most common nesting duck. Thus, this species of duck was chosen as a subject of study in order to obtain data to form the basis for waterfowl management in Iowa.

SYSTEMATIC POSITION

The Blue-winged Teal is a species of the genus *Querquedula*, one of 11 North American genera of surface-feeding ducks clasified in the subfamily Anatinae. There is one other species in the genus *Querquedula* found in North America, the Cinnamon Teal (*Querquedula cyanoptera* (Vieillot)). The bright chestnut-cinnamon color of the male Cinnamon Teal and its slightly larger size easily distinguishes it from the brown-feathered male Blue-winged Teal. Although the female Cinnamon Teal and the Blue-winged Teal female are similar in size and color, the chestnut-tinted breast and abdomen feathers of the former distinguish it from the latter.

---

[1] The scientific name of the bird as given in the American Ornithologists' Union *Check-list of North American Birds,* fourth edition, 1931.

The systematic position of the Blue-winged Teal is as follows:

Class Aves
Subclass Neornithes
Superorder Neognathae
Order Anseriformes
Suborder Anseres
Family Anatidae
Subfamily Anatinae
Genus *Querquedula*
Species *Q. discors*

VERNACULAR NAMES

Blue-winged Teal is the correct common name of *Querquedula discors* as listed in the American Ornithologists' Union's *Check-list of North American Birds,* 1931. Throughout the breeding, migratory and wintering range the bird is known by a number of names. Following are listed vernacular names applied to the Blue-winged Teal.

Name	Locality	Authority
autonniere	Louisiana	McAtee, 1934
azulejo	Guatemala	Phillips, 1923
blauflugelige krickente	German	Phillips, 1923
blauflugelige streinte	German	Phillips, 1923
blauwvleugeltaling	Dutch	Phillips, 1923
blue-winged teal	Universal	McAtee, 1934
blue-wing	Universal	McAtee, 1934
butterball	Maine	McAtee, 1934
cercelle	French	Phillips, 1923
chichi pato	Mexican (Maya Indian)	E. A. & L. J. Goldman (unpublished)
fall duck	Cree Indian	C. E. Gillham (unpublished)
fall teal	Mississippi	McAtee, 1934
la sarcelle a ailes bleues	Canada	Taverner, 1934
Louisiana blue-winged teal	Louisiana	McAtee, 1934
lunate bluewing	Jamaica	Gosse, 1847
melzcanauhtli	Mexican	Phillips, 1923
neck-tie teal	Missouri	Author
patillo	Spanish	Phillips, 1923
pato celecal	West Indies	Bond, 1936
pato de la Florida	West Indies	Bond, 1936
printanniere	Louisiana	McAtee, 1934
sarcelle	West Indies	Bond, 1936
sarcelle a ailes bleues	Southern U. S.	McAtee, 1934
sarcelle a croissants	Trinidad	Chapman, 1894
sarcelle d'ete	Louisiana	McAtee, 1934
sarcelle autonniere	Louisiana	McAtee, 1934
sarcelle printanniere	Louisiana	McAtee, 1934

Name	Locality	Authority
sarcelle d'Amerique	Southern U. S.	McAtee, 1934
sarcelle de Cayenne	French	Phillips, 1923
sarcelle soucrourou	French	Phillips, 1923
sarcelle soucrourette	French	Phillips, 1923
southern teal	Missouri	Author
summer teal	Delaware	McAtee, 1934
teal	Universal	McAtee, 1934
teal duck	Universal	McAtee, 1934
toltecoltl	Mexican	Phillips, 1923
white-crested teal	Southern U. S.	McAtee, 1934
whiteface	Southern U. S.	McAtee, 1934
white-faced teal	Iowa (Spring)	Author
white-faced teal	Southern U. S.	McAtee, 1934
white-faced duck	Southern U. S.	McAtee, 1934
we-wi-bing-guang-ge	Chippewa Indian	Cooke, 1884
zarceta	Mexico	E. A. & L. J. Goldman (unpublished)
zarceta de ala azul	Mexico	E. A. & L. J. Goldman (unpublished)
zarceta de verano	Mexico	E. A. & L. J. Goldman (unpublished)
zarceta tulera	Mexico	E. A. & L. J. Goldman (unpublished)
zarceta de invierno	Spanish	Phillips, 1923
zarceta de stono	Spanish	Phillips, 1923

SEX RATIO

The sex ratio of 5,090 Blue-winged Teal observed during the fall flight, on the wintering grounds and during the 1932-36 spring flights averaged 59 percent males and 41 percent females (table I). The fall sex determinations were made only on bagged birds as the plumage between females and males is indistinguishable in flight at that season of the year. The wintering ground counts were made in Mexico on birds that were definitely distinguishable males or females in the wild state and on birds checked in the market places. The spring flight counts were made in Iowa after all birds had acquired their breeding plumage.

The breeding ground counts were made after the nesting season had started. The ratio of the breeding birds in Iowa was 52 males to 48 females, whereas Furniss' (1935) counts on the breeding grounds of Saskatchewan, Canada, indicated 58 percent males and 42 percent females. Perhaps the unmated males on the southern edge of the breeding range move northward to spend the summer as unmated birds.

Only a small sample of ducklings was taken during the study period. Very little collecting was done in the Ruthven area during the rearing season because of possible unfavorable public reactions. There was no outbreak of disease or severe parasitism to warrant collecting for those purposes. Thirty-six ducklings were collected during 1932-36. The sex ratio was 58 percent males and 42 percent females. Although the 36 ducklings represented a very small sample, the sex ratio percentages corresponded quite closely to those data on migratory and wintering birds.

TABLE I. *Sex ratio of Blue-winged Teal*

Time and place	No. of males	Percentage	No. of females	Percentage
Fall flight, Iowa—1933	151	61.7	94	38.3
Fall flight, Iowa—1936	8	57.2	6	42.8
Winter, Mexico—1936-37	1250	59.6	850	40.4
Spring flight, Iowa—1935	647	57.8	474	42.2
Spring flight, Iowa—1936	938	59.6	636	40.4
Breeding, Iowa—1932-36	762	52.3	699	47.7
Breeding grounds, Saskatchewan, Canada—1935	38	58	26	42
Ducklings, Iowa—1932-36	21	58.4	15	41.6

WEIGHTS

Thirty-six Blue-winged Teal were examined from the wintering grounds in Mexico, December, 1936, and January, 1937. All of the birds examined were in good condition and fat. Thirteen of the 36 birds were weighed; the average weight of the males was 370 grams, the average weight of the females, 346 grams.

Average weights for 12 birds collected and weighed during the 1935 fall flight through Iowa were 353 grams for the males and 315 grams for the females; for 13 teal collected and weighed during the spring flights of 1933-35 through Iowa, 359 grams for the males and 356 grams for the females; for 9 summer adults collected during July-August, 1933-36, 353 grams for the males and 314 grams for the females.

Fourteen juveniles were collected during 1933-36 and weighed to determine an indication of the weight progression and weight of young birds at the start of the fall migration period. The heaviest young male weighed 320 grams August 16, and the heaviest young female weighed 315 grams on the same date.

The heaviest adult males were noted on the wintering grounds, averaging 370 grams each. The heaviest females were recorded just prior to the nesting season, averaging 356 grams each. The lightest males were those collected during the spring flight and during the eclipse plumage stage, averaging 353 grams each for both periods. The females weighing the least were those weighed during the rearing season, averaging 314 grams each. During all months of the year the males weighed more than the females (table II).

TABLE II. *Weights of the Blue-winged Teal*

Wintering grounds Mexico, December, 1936-January, 1937		
Number	Males	Females
	Grams	Grams
1	375	360
2	400	340
3	370	350
4	375	325
5	300	350
6	390	350
7	380	
Average weight	370	346

Fall flight Iowa, October-November, 1935		
Number	Males	Females
	Grams	Grams
1	290	300
2	310	320
3	375	360
4	415	310
5	390	320
6	360	280
Average weight	353	315

Spring flight Iowa, April-May, 1933-35		
Number	Males	Females
	Grams	Grams
1	375	300
2	300	360
3	410	380
4	400	375
5	325	360
6	360	360
7	345	
Average weight	359	356

Summer adults
Iowa, July-August, 1933-36

Number	Males	Females
	Grams	Grams
1	350	310
2	360	315
3	370	340
4	325	290
5	360	
Average weight	353	314

Juveniles, first summer
Iowa, July-August, 1933-36

Number	Date	Males	Females
		Grams	Grams
1	July 22		187.5
2	27	295	
3	31	304	201
4	31	365	326
5	31	271.5	
6	Aug. 2	310	280
7	16	320	315
8	21	300	290

PLUMAGES

Downy Young. Upon hatching the young teal is clothed in wet natal down. Within three hours the ducklings become dry, and the soft downy feathers expose their true colors. Bent (1923, p. 115) gives the following description of the downy young: "In the downy young the colors of the upper parts vary from 'mummy' brown to 'Dresden brown,' darker on the crown and rump, lighter elsewhere, the down being much darker basally; the under parts are 'maize yellow,' shaded locally with 'buff yellow,' due to the darker tips of the down; the sides of the head are 'yellow ocher' or pale 'buckthorn brown' in young birds, but these colors soon fade and all the colors grow paler as the young bird increases in size. The color pattern of the head consists of a dark-brown central crown bordered on each side by a broad superciliary stripe of yellow ocher, below which is a narrow postocular stripe, a loral patch and an auricular spot of dusky. On the back the brown is broken by large spots of yellowish, one on each side of the rump and one on each scapular region."

Juveniles, First Summer. Following the down stage, the

brown, mottled feathers on the sides of the abdomen are the first to appear. These feathers become noticeable about two weeks after hatching, and their growth spreads around the breast and then over the back and head. The down feathers disappear last on the head and rump, and by the end of July the spotted juvenal body plumage is complete. Late in July the wing and tail feathers develop and shortly after these grow out the young birds begin to fly. By mid-August most of the young are flying or in the act of learning. The sexes of the young cannot be distinguished by the plumage at this age as they resemble the adult females.

Juveniles, Fall and Early Winter. The young, both sexes, continue to resemble the adult females, the lesser wing coverts and green speculum being somewhat more dull than that of the adult and the underparts more streaked and speckled.

Juveniles, Late Winter and Spring. The young females are hardly distinguishable from adult females, but the plumage of the young female is not quite so glossy as that of the adult.

The males acquire the nuptial plumage between the last of December and March 15. The colors of the first-year males are slightly less bright than those of the older birds.

Juveniles, Second Summer. The young acquire the complete adult plumage during the second summer, and they cannot be distinguished from older birds at this time by the plumage.

Adults, Winter and Spring. The males begin showing their nuptial plumage during December. By March the molt is complete and the males are in full nuptial plumage. The change is gradual, since the white crescent in front of the eye shows very faintly at first. About the time the crescent shows very clearly the head and upper neck begin to show the dark purplish-black nuptial feathers. The white lateral rump patch spots become evident at approximately the same time that the neck and head feathers replace the dusky brown feathers. Along with the development of the white crescent, purplish neck and head feathers, and white rump patches the breast and belly become heavily spotted with chestnut-brown feathers.

The females molt into a new plumage with the males, but the plumage colors change only slightly, about the only difference being brighter and cleaner plumage.

The frontispiece is a reproduction of a plate showing a pair of Blue-winged Teal in breeding plumage. The female is illustrated without the blue in the wings because the blue in the wings, both female and male, is covered by the brown wing coverts in a natural standing, sitting or swimming position. The only time that the blue is evident is when the birds are flying, preening, relaxing or stretching, or when the wing coverts are stuck back by mud, vegetation or water. To illustrate the wing and belly feather colors, the male is shown in a preening position.

Adults, Summer. The male birds have a postnuptial molt into eclipse plumage that begins soon after they desert the incubating females. Most of the males lose their gay nuptial dress between June 20 and August 1. The eclipse plumage lasts until October or longer. During this stage the males are hardly discernible from the females, the main difference being in the brighter blue in the wings.

The female begins to molt into eclipse plumage during the spring that is completed into breeding plumage the following spring.

HYBRIDS

Swarth (1915) recorded the apparent crossbreeding of a pair of ducks of the genera *Spatula* and *Querquedula.* He based his conclusions on the characters of one specimen that showed quite clearly the characters of both genera.

The author has not observed in the field or museum specimens of the Blue-winged Teal that showed evidences of crossbreeding with other species.

PLUMAGE VARIATIONS

Kennard (1919) described a subspecies of the Blue-winged Teal. The promulgated name was *Querquedula discors albinucha.* The basis for the description was the white crescent of the male in nuptial plumage extending over the eyes and joining at the back of the head to form a white nuchal spot in birds that apparently nested in the southern part of the United States. This subspecific determination was not accepted by the American Ornithologists' Union (Oberholser, 1921) on the basis that the evidence presented indicated a difference of age or a color phase. The author examined several hundred specimens from Mexico and the United States. It was common to find specimens with the white crescent extending back over the eyes and joining. On some specimens the feathers had to be parted before the few white feathers extending backward could be seen. On other specimens the markings were quite distinct. The author confirms the opinion of the American Orntihologists' Union that the presence of the white nuchal spot is merely a variation in plumage coloration.

CHAPTER II

Breeding Range

The early settlers of the upper Mississippi Valley reported seeing thousands of ducks of many species on the sloughs and marshes of the Great Plains. Indians from the prairies to the west and east of the Mississippi River told of unbelievable numbers of ducks, geese and other marsh birds. Although the ornithological information in these reports is fragmentary, it gives a hazy idea of waterfowl productivity of the prairie country at that time.

With the advent of the Louisiana Purchase in 1803 that broad expanse of virgin territory was made available to thousands of pioneers. It soon became known to the people of many nationalities that much of the land purchased from Spain could be plowed and made to produce a crop the first season. A decade later settlers found the same rich country in the prairie provinces of Canada. From that time until the present the lands of the Louisiana Purchase and Canada have been exploited, many times as a detriment to the welfare of the countries.

Today the State of Minnesota is called the state of ten thousand lakes. In 1800 the territory that was to be known as Iowa, Illinois, Missouri, South Dakota, North Dakota, Minnesota, Saskatchewan, Alberta and Manitoba could have been called the country of ten million potholes. It was on those potholes and marshes that the Blue-winged Teal thrived. At that time about 50 percent of the Blue-winged Teal production was in land that was to become a part of the United States. The other 50 percent was produced in the prairie areas of Canada (fig. 3).

The A. O. U. *Check-list* (1931, p. 48) lists the breeding range for the Blue-winged Teal as follows: "Breeds from central British Columbia, Great Slave Lake, northern Saskatchewan, central Manitoba, southern Ontario, New Brunswick, Maine, and Rhode Island south to western New York (rarely Long Island and eastern Pensylvania), Ohio, Indiana, Illinois, central Missouri, central Kansas, Northern New Mexico, central Utah and northern Nevada (has bred in Florida, Louisiana, Texas and Oklahoma)."

Since 1900, principally in the United States, extensive and intensive agriculture has eliminated a large proportion of the breeding grounds. The rapid advance of agriculture affected adversely both directly and indirectly the prairie country as a duck-producing habitat. The drainage of marshes and the plowing, grazing and mowing of adjacent prairies eliminated directly the breeding grounds. The straightening of streams and the denuding of land of permanent vegetation caused a gradual lowering of water tables that further restricted the breeding range. One of the most vivid examples of this is Devil's Lake, North Dakota. In 1900 the lake, a veritable paradise for breeding ducks, began to undergo a decline. Today the water is almost gone, and a stagnant pool of alkaline water is all that is left. In 1900 duck hunters could stand in front of the railway station and partake of the sport of shooting ducks. The remaining water cannot be seen from that railway station today. A severe drought that was climaxed in 1934 practically destroyed, at least for the present, the greater part of the duck breeding grounds in the United States and the southern parts of the prairie provinces of Canada. However, some of these remnants may be rehabilitated to a certain extent by rainfall of normal years. On this basis the present breeding area of the Blue-winged Teal is given (fig. 4). It is estimated that in 1935 about 80 percent of the Blue-winged Teal was produced in Canada. The 80 percent produced in Canada in 1935 was actually a much smaller number of ducks than was produced in the same area in 1900. Probably not more than 25 percent of the 1900 numbers was produced in 1935.

Agriculture has gained a permanent foothold in Alberta, Saskatchewan, Manitoba and British Columbia. Since 1900 much of the southern halves of those provinces has become

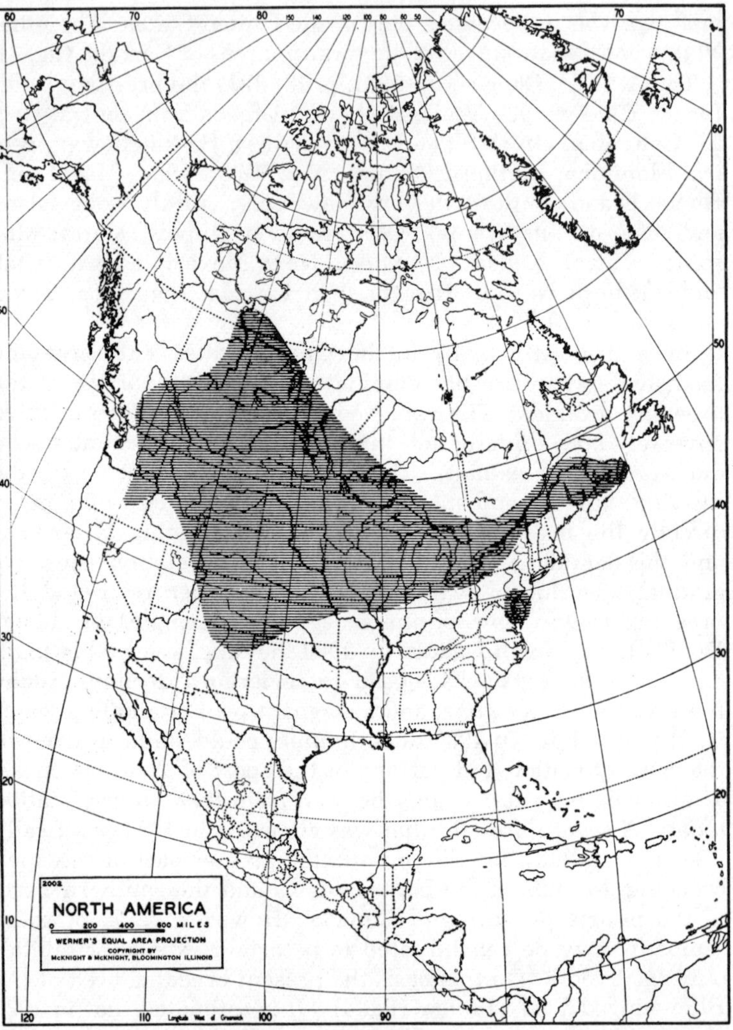

FIG. 3. Breeding range of the Blue-winged Teal. Large nesting populations were found throughout the cross-hatched region in the United States and Canada prior to 1900.

world famous for grain production. Thousands of acres of nesting grounds have been depleted by the plow and by grazing.

It is a general opinion among many people that there are hundreds of thousands of acres suitable for Blue-winged Teal breeding all over Canada and even though all of the prairie marshes in the United States are destroyed we should continue to have shootable numbers of this bird. The Blue-winged Teal, like most other animals, has a definite breeding range. The prairie-type marshes seem to be a requirement for the well being of this bird. Just why this teal does not breed abundantly in the forest lake areas or the barren lands of the north is not clearly known. Therefore, the breeding grounds cannot continue to be destroyed and at the same time produce a yearly surplus of shootable birds. Some of the factors that may control the breeding range are dealt with in this thesis.

After knowing the limits of the breeding range and the conversion of a large part of it from a waterfowl production area into one of the greatest agricultural regions in the world, it is not difficult to visualize why the numbers of migrating Blue-winged Teal have become less and less since 1900.

TYPES OF BREEDING AREAS

The types of breeding areas have been classified by the author on the basis of plant formations. There are five distinct breeding area types in the breeding range segregated by this classification. Following they are listed and discussed in the order of their importance as production units.

1. *The True Prairie Area*

The true prairie area includes Manitoba, western Minnesota, eastern North Dakota, eastern South Dakota, western Iowa, eastern Nebraska, eastern Kansas and Oklahoma. The more important plants found in this area originally were beard grasses *(Andropogon scoparius)* and *(A. furcatus)*[1], needle grass *(Stipa comata)*, porcupine grass *(S. spartea)*, drop-seed grass *(Sporobolus asper)*, Koeler's grass *(Koeleria cristata)*, mesquite grass *(Bouteloua curtipendula)* and buffalo grass *(Buchloe dactyloides)*. These plants must have furnished excellent nesting cover prior to the taking over of the plains by the white man. Today most of this rich prairie vegetation has been removed by cultivation and overgrazing. In northwestern Iowa not more than one percent of the true prairie remains. The existing prairie plots are usually less than 10 acres in size and are found on knolls too rocky to plow.

This rolling prairie was originally interspersed with myriads of potholes, sloughs, marshes and lakes. The prairie grasses

[1] The scientific plant names used in this book are taken from Gray's *New Manual of Botany*, fourth edition, 1908.

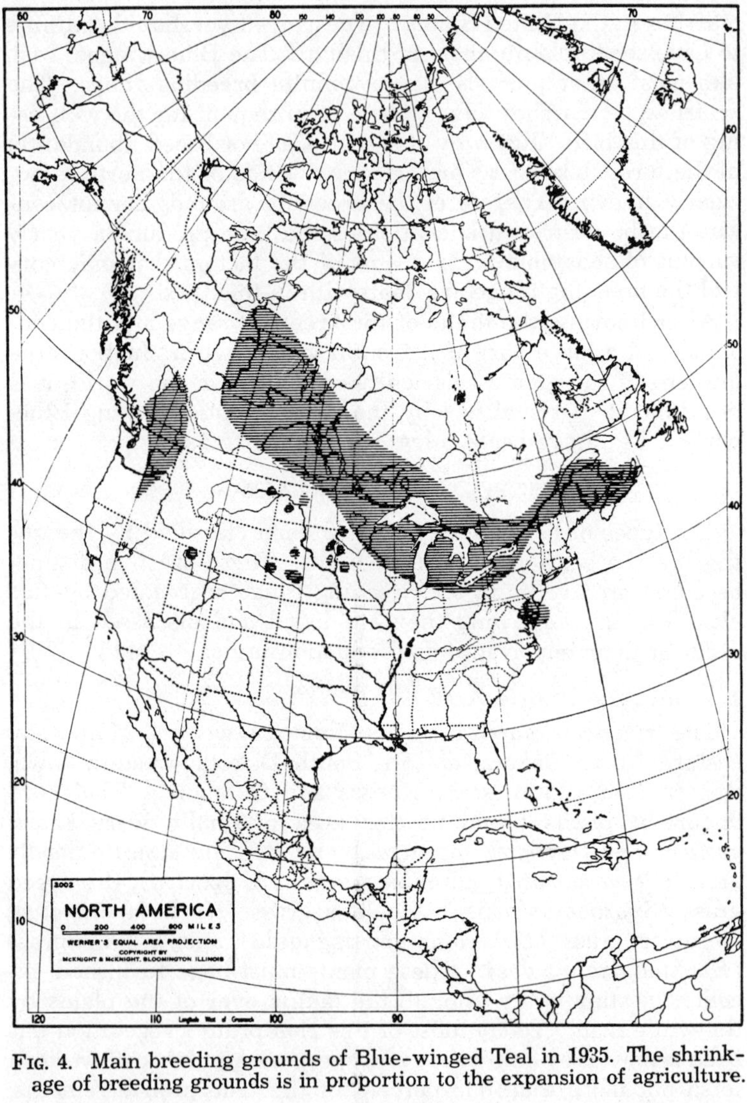

FIG. 4. Main breeding grounds of Blue-winged Teal in 1935. The shrinkage of breeding grounds is in proportion to the expansion of agriculture.

furnished the nesting cover. Bluegrass *(Poa pratensis)* is the dominant plant providing nesting cover in northwestern Iowa today. This condition was brought about by the grazing of the prairie bordering the existing water areas.

2. *Mixed Prairie*

The mixed prairie area extends from northern Alberta and northern Saskatchewan to the plains of Texas. It is found east to central South Dakota, central North Dakota and south to Oklahoma. The western border is in western Wyoming and eastern Utah. Most of this area, due to grazing, has only two dominant genera of grasses today. They are the short grasses, *Bouteloua* and *Buchloe*. Although this area was at one time a great duck-producing area, the southern half of the region supports but few water areas at present. This great expanse of territory is now known as the *short grass plains.*

3. *Boreal Forest Area*

Blue-winged Teal are found nesting in the boreal forest area from Great Slave Lake south to the prairie area, southeast to the Great Lakes region, and east to Maine, Nova Scotia and New Brunswick. This territory composes the northern limit of the nesting range of the Blue-winged Teal. Many of these birds are produced from the great plains north to Great Slave Lake. The nesting populations become less numerous east of Manitoba.

E. A. Preble (1908) gives the status of the Blue-winged Teal in the Athabaska-Mackenzie region as follows: "This duck is a rather rare or local summer resident north to Great Slave Lake. Ross recorded it as being found north to Fort Resolution, but as being rare. Kennicott noted one at Fort Resolution, May 7, 1860, and a specimen taken by him there June 8, 1860, is still in the National Museum. The Museum catalogue also records a specimen collected at Fort Simpson. J. Alden Loring found the species common at Edmonton, Alberta, in September, 1894, and on the trail between Edmonton and Jasper House in the early autumn of 1895. In the spring of 1897 Spreadborough found it common at Edmonton. It was first observed April 28, was common by May 3, and a nest was found May 19. MacFarlane, in a list recently sent me, states that a nest containing three eggs was found by an Indian near Fort Providence on June 1, 1885. H. W. Jones, by letter, reports this teal from Hay River, Great Slave Lake, where he observed three pairs in the summer of 1907."

4. *Deciduous Forest Area*

This breeding area in the deciduous forest area extends from central Iowa through Minnesota, Illinois, the southern half of

Wisconsin, Ohio, Indiana, Maryland, Delaware, Pennsylvania and New York. Throughout this forest area lakes, rivers and marshes are found. Some prairie marsh areas are found interspersed through the region, particularly in Iowa, Illinois, Indiana and Ohio. In these areas the Blue-winged Teal is still found nesting in limited numbers. Scattered nesting also takes place in the vicinity of the Great Lakes and the upper Mississippi River. The water areas in this region are only secondary Blue-winged Teal production areas.

Recent literature concerning the avifauna of this region almost unanimously states that the Blue-winged Teal is not as common as formerly. However, Hicks (1935) is of the opinion that the bird has been increasing as a breeding bird in Ohio the past few years.

5. *Lake Forest Area*

The lake forest area is confined around the Great Lakes and eastward to New England. A few nesting Blue-winged Teal are recorded throughout the region each year.

CHAPTER III

Fall Migration

The coming of Indian summer in August, from 1932 to 1936, brought forth the first Blue-winged Teal from the North. On those hazy days while the leaves of trees and shrubs were turning from green to more gorgeous colors this duck was seen nervously congregating in small flocks on the sloughs and lakes where rank growths of bulrushes *(Scirpus* spp.*)*, arrowheads *(Sagittaria* spp.*)*, and pondweeds *(Potamogeton* spp.*)* were found.

It would be rather difficult to determine on what date the earliest fall migrants arrived in Iowa as many were reared in northwestern section of the state. However, the last two weeks in August and the early days of September always witnessed an increase in the Blue-winged Teal populations. The southward flight was leisurely and was hastened only as the nights slowly became colder. The shooting season seemed to have but little effect upon the length of time spent in migration. In 1935 the shooting season did not open until October 19, by which time a large proportion of the birds had already migrated to the south of Iowa. The previous year the season opened on October 1. The number of teal taken in hunters' bags on October 19 in 1935 was a much smaller number than obtained on the opening day October 1, 1934. However, where state lines form boundaries on shooting dates there were local migratory stimuli brought about by shooting.

The flight in general began in the North about the last week in August and approximately six to eight weeks were spent in reaching the wintering grounds in the Southland. The Blue-winged Teal, true to its classification as a puddle duck, was found in the largest numbers all along the migratory route on

FIG. 5. Mud Lake, Clay County, Iowa. A bulrush marsh utilized by thousands of teal during migration. (Photo by H. H. Knight.)

shallow sloughs, marshes, ponds, lakes, rivers and in the bayous and lagoons of the larger bodies of water (fig. 5). In those shallow waters they found the food that they can easily obtain by their dabbling feeding methods.

The flight through Iowa was usually completed by the first week in November. In 1932 Bennett (1933) checked the fall flight of ducks through Clay and Palo Alto Counties, Iowa. On that year the heaviest flight took place from October 15 to October 22. The birds were present in lesser numbers until forced out of the region by a blizzard on November 8. In 1936 the main flight passed through Iowa between September and October 10. On the opening day of the shooting season in 1936, November 1, several thousand ducks were seen but no Blue-winged Teal were observed among them.

Weather conditions were apparently not the primary reasons why the Blue-winged Teal moved southward. Most of the flight was over in the North long before food became inaccessible by the freezing over of water areas. Because the shortage of foods did not occur, such a factor was not responsible for the abandonment of the northern areas. In Iowa the food supply found in the remaining potholes, marshes, sloughs and lakes[1] was practically untouched, even after the entire waterfowl flight had passed. It was true, however, that some of the deeper Iowa lakes had but a small quantity of desirable duck foods in them. The shortage of foods was a result of the unfavorable conditions in the lakes for the propagation of those food plants.

[1] Water area terms used in this book are defined as follows: *A pothole* is a swamp area 12 acres or less in size. *A slough* is a swamp area more than 12 acres in size and with a width less than one-third its length. *A marsh* is a swamp area more than 12 acres in size whose width is more than one-third its length. *A lake* is a body of water devoid of emergent vegetation.

The Iowa lakes and marshes, with the exception of the deep water lakes, had an almost unlimited supply of ideal puddle duck foods.

Within the main breeding areas the flocks of Blue-winged Teal consisted of several hundred birds at the beginning of the migration period. Entire broods of several families quite often flocked together on the prairie marshes the latter part of the rearing season. In other instances the adoption of other broods by a single female also resulted in large local flocks. On August 21, 1933, the author observed 1 female leading 42 juveniles of several ages, ranging from flightless birds of four weeks old to birds that had been flying for several weeks. This flock of young birds probably represented six or seven broods.

SHOOTING SEASON

On the opening day of the shooting season those birds that had become unsuspicious through the unmolested days of summer were bewildered by the storm of powder and lead. It was during the first few days of the hunting season that the largest number of teal were taken by hunters in the North (prior to 1936). Practically the entire flight had passed through Iowa in 1936 by the date the shooting season opened.

The experiences lost and gained by this little duck on the inauguration of the shooting season were sad. As the time of day set for the opening of the season approached, when almost every marsh had its brown-clad wildfowlers anxiously counting the minutes, a few overzealous or "fast-watch" shots were fired. That pretime shooting was usually scattered enough to start most of the birds flying. A few minutes later, sometimes seconds, the greater majority of ducks met a hail of lead. Most of the hunters were out of practice, not having fired their guns for several months, and, although many ducks were killed during the first spell of firing the losses were not nearly so great as one might expect.

The teal became wary after about one-half hour of shooting on the opening day. The lessened numbers soon learned to "climb" into the sky several hundred yards to avoid the persecution. Several hours were spent in aimless flying over marshes, sloughs, potholes and lakes. After numerous attempts to come down, those that escaped either stayed in the air at safe distance, found refuge or alighted in the middle of large open bodies of water where they obtained at least temporary safety.

In some lake areas the state or federal government had established refuges. It was surprising how soon those areas were recognized as havens of safety. After the shooting had ceased at sundown, or at whatever hour the regulations called for, the ducks slowly learned that for some reason or other the sedges and cat-tails were again safe. Several preliminary attempts were made at alighting on the water before they were assured that peace was with them for the deepening dusk and night.

The large flocks of one to five hundred individuals were dispersed with the coming of the shooting season. Whether shooting was entirely responsible for the breaking up of the larger flocks into smaller ones the author cannot say. The majority of migrating flocks were composed of less than 30 birds. Many times singles and doubles were observed on their southward journey. Such individuals or couplets may have been remnants of larger flocks or birds that had become lost from a flock.

FLYWAYS

From the northern breeding marshes the birds followed in general the main waterways to the wintering grounds. Throughout the migration routes in Canada and the United States the birds were hunted for sport. Food and water conditions changed as the birds flew toward their wintering grounds. The bulrush marsh of the North had little in common with a cypress swamp of the South. However, as far as food was concerned, the teal used and thrived in both types of feeding areas.

When the last of the teal flight was passing from the North, sometimes early cold weather brought about rough water on the larger lakes, marshes and rivers. During such periods the teal sought out the little streamlets, creeks and drainage ditches whose waters were more or less protected. It was at such times that the "jump shooter" had good hunting away from the larger bodies of water.

The major portion of the flight was in the Mississippi Valley and the Central Flyways. As the Mississippi Valley Flyway comprised a much larger area of the choice breeding range of the Blue-winged Teal, it was found that the largest numbers utlized this route (fig. 6). A minor percentage of the population migrated by way of the Pacific and Atlantic Flyways. There was some crossing over from one flyway to the other, but to what extent this occurred is not clearly known.

Some birds take a southeasterly course from the Canadian

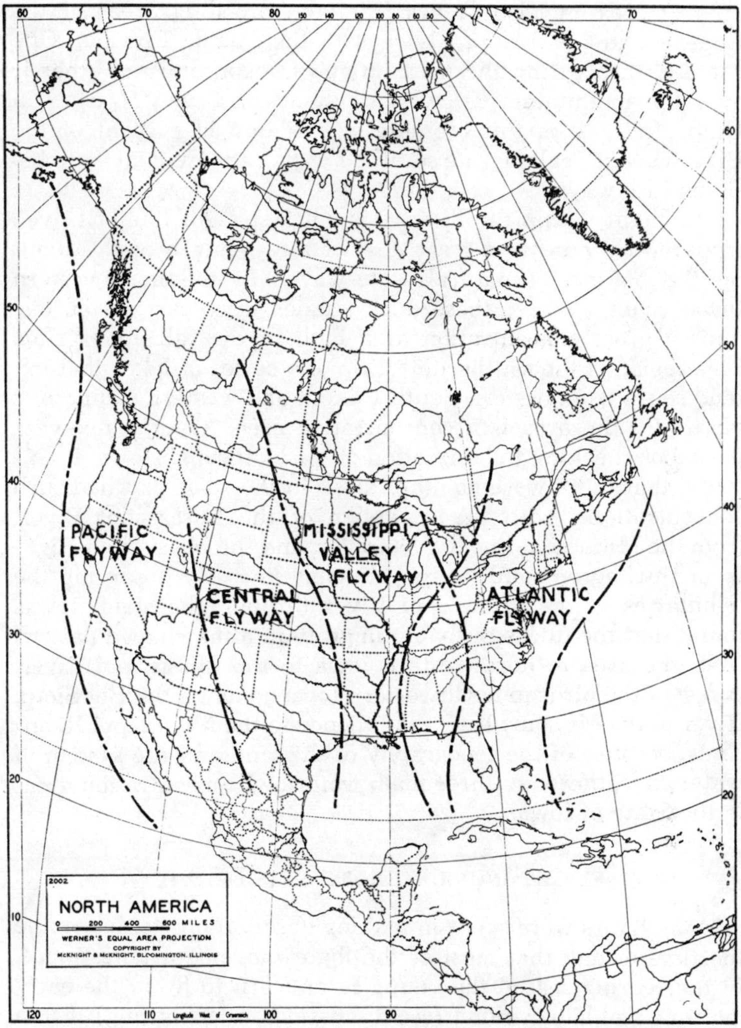

Fig. 6. The major waterfowl flyways.

breeding grounds that lie in the Central and Mississippi Flyways and fly down the Atlantic Coast. Phillips and Lincoln (1930) tell of another cross-over channel that diverges from the Mississippi Flyway at the mouth of the Illinois River. The birds that take this route cross the mountains of Tennessee and Kentucky and reach the coast of South Carolina. A certain degree of crossing also occurs from the breeding areas of the Central and Mississippi Flyways to the Pacific Flyway. One route is through northern Idaho and Oregon and the other is over the mountains just west of the Bear River Marshes in Utah. In spite of this crossing over about 90 percent of the Blue-winged Teal migrate south by way of the Central and Mississippi Flyways.

The flight within the flyways is not a straight line of travel. Apparently there is a great deal of zigzagging brought about by the pattern of natural waterways. In the northwestern Iowa locality, where these duck studies were carried on, one finds a great concentration area both in the fall and spring. This region is the southernmost tip of a series of lakes that extend south from eastern South Dakota and western Minnesota. Naturally the area is a concentration area. Over a five-year period of checking the migration of ducks through Iowa, it was found that there were no other areas in the state that had such concentrations, with the exception of the Mississippi River, from the Minnesota line to McGregor, and the Mississippi River from Burlington south to the Missouri line. By observing the tributaries of the Mississippi River through the state it was found that the ducks probably migrate in a fan-shaped pattern from the area in northwestern Iowa to the Mississippi River. A few of the birds in northwestern Iowa go down the Big Sioux River to the Missouri River and thence to the Mississippi River. Thus, because of the topography of the land and the system of waterways, there are three main waterfowl concentration areas in the State of Iowa.

FLIGHT IN RELATION TO TIME OF DAY

Many hours were spent in making observations to determine the time of day that most of the flight movement takes place. In the rearing season the young birds learn to fly in the early morning and late evening (see discussion under rearing). From the time the birds first begin to fly they spend some time each morning and evening flying over their rearing grounds. Whether this flying is restlessness or practice would be difficult to ascertain; perhaps it is a combination of both.

In many localities these birds that migrate into an area by dawn or darkness are mistaken for locally reared birds. The author is familiar with one small lake area that actually produces about 500 ducks, but by September 10 several thousand can be seen there. As the birds move in overnight and their coming is not noticed, the local people assume with pride that the birds are home-raised. Thus, many areas are overvalued as to their duck production.

The early morning and late evening flying becomes more apparent as the time of migration approaches. The actual migration appears to be an outgrowth of the flight training period. Practically all of the early migration is done early in the morning and late in the evening. From October 15, when early cold periods are sometimes encountered in Iowa, migrating flocks may be observed at any hour of the day or night.

DROUGHT IN RELATION TO MIGRATION

Throughout the duration of these studies drought conditions were prevalent in the prairie areas. The drought conditions brought about a change in migratory duck populations in Iowa. The water areas in northwest Iowa maintained a more or less normal water level in spite of long dry periods. Lake areas in South Dakota, North Dakota, Nebraska and Wyoming suffered greatly. Many of the choice nesting and resting areas dried up. It is known that the Blue-winged Teal probably suffered as greatly as any other species of duck throughout the drought area. However, in 1934, and 1936, the climax periods of the drought to date, a noticeable increase in migrating teal was observed in the lake areas of Iowa. Those local increases merely indicated that the birds were forced to traverse different routes of flight in times of necessity. Local increases in favorable duck hunting areas brought about by adverse conditions elsewhere often lead many groups of sportsmen and conservationists to derive false conclusions concerning the status of the species. Those people who are entrusted with the task of setting seasons and bag limits are well aware of such discrepancies that arise from local conditions.

DAILY LENGTH OF FLIGHT

Although the Blue-winged Teal may assume a speed of more than fifty miles per hour, the daily mileage southward is rather low. Undoubtedly many stops are made for feeding and resting. Individual birds or flocks of birds may at times travel several hundred miles per day. However, banding observations indicate that this is not done day after day throughout the flight. Lincoln (1936, p. 143) recorded a Blue-winged Teal that was banded in Quebec, Canada, Sept. 5, 1930, and was killed Oct. 2, 1930, in British Guiana, an airline distance of about 2,400 miles from the point of banding. The bird flew at least 85 miles a day for 28 days to cover the distance in that length of time.

SPEED OF FLIGHT

Many fantastic tales of the flying speed of ducks have been told since man first became interested in them. The Blue-winged Teal has always been regarded as a very fast flier. Its small size further accentuates its speed in the eyes of the casual observer. It was found by checking the speed of these birds with automobiles that rarely did the speed range over 45 miles per hour. On one occasion two birds were paced at 48 miles per hour.

Most of the migrating birds observed were traveling at varying speeds between 30 and 40 miles per hour. Of course, flight aided by strong tail winds would increase the speed considerably. However, all winds are not favorable to flying teal. In several instances the author observed teal flying against strong head winds and making only one, two, or three miles per hour, sometimes even losing ground. The teal do not buffet such adverse winds very long. Throughout the duration of strong head-on winds they rest in the less turbulent habitat of the marsh or bayou.

FLIGHT ALTITUDES

The height at which the Blue-winged Teal migrate varies greatly. Many individuals and flocks were observed apparently migrating over chains of lakes from 10 feet to 500 feet above the water. Over the same series of lakes birds have been observed that were flying close to 5,000 feet. Observations made on the Mississippi River from the Minnesota line to the Missouri line lead the author to believe that most of the teal pass down that river at an altitude of 500 to 1,000 feet. Of course, birds might fly at one level for a period and then rise or descend to a different height due to weather conditions, topography of the land, shooting or unknown causes.

Lincoln (1935, p. 23) states that bird migration in general is performed below an altitude of 3,000 feet. The author's observations confirm this statement for the Blue-winged Teal.

MIGRATION COMPANIONSHIP WITH OTHER WATERFOWL

From the time the ducklings hatched they were more or less in rather close association with other animals on the rearing grounds. At the beginning of the migration season it was not uncommon to see Blue-winged Teal feeding and flying with Common Mallard *(Anas platyrhynchos platyrhynchos)*, Gadwall *(Chaulelasmus streperus)*, Baldpate *(Mareca americana)*, American Pintail *(Dafila acuta tzitzihoa)*, Green-winged Teal *(Nettion carolinense)*, Shoveller *(Spatula clypeata)*, Redhead *(Nyroca americana)*, Ring-necked Duck *(Nyroca collaris)*, Canvas-back *(Nyroca valisineria)*, Lesser Scaup *(Nyroca affinis)*, Ruddy Duck *(Erismatura jamaicensis rubida)*, American Coot *(Fulica americana americana)* or shore birds *(Charadriidae)*. As a rule, after the flight had begun in earnest the Blue-winged Teal migrated by themselves. Occasionally a lone teal was observed flying with a flock of Mallards or with some other species of duck. On several occasions a lone American Coot and a lone Pied-billed Grebe *(Podilymbus podiceps podiceps)* were recorded migrating with a flock of teal. Almost every possible combination of migrating ducks was observed during the fall flights. However, the greater proportion of Blue-winged Teal preferred to migrate with their own kind.

CHAPTER IV

Wintering Grounds

The wintering grounds of the Blue-winged Teal extend over thousands of square miles in Mexico, Central America, South America and the southern part of the United States (fig. 7).

Cooke (1906, p. 33) gives the wintering range as follows: "Blue-winged Teal migrate over a vast extent of territory, and are found in winter throughout northern South America south to Brazil, Ecuador, Peru and Chile. They occur abundantly in Central America, Mexico and the West Indies, and are equally common during the winter in the Gulf States and north to North Carolina. In the Mississippi Valley few remain much north of the Gulf, though these few are scattered widely as far as southern Indiana and southern Illinois; a few winter in Arizona, and a small number of Pacific Coast birds spend the winter in California and north to southern British Columbia."

Since the time of Cook's publication there have been numerous state bird lists written giving the distribution of resident and migrant birds. The Blue-winged Teal is not listed as an abundant winter resident in any of the state lists or in any other recent publication. Howell (1911) in *Birds of Arkansas* says, "In mild winters a few remain in the state as in the winter of 1893-94, when they were reported in small numbers from Big Lake." The author observed several small flocks on the Mississippi River near Rush Tower, Mo., in January, 1926, and January, 1931. These birds may have been cripples that recovered or exceedingly early migrants. Dr. Harry C. Oberholser, of the United States Bureau of Biological Survey, informed the writer in 1936 that a few teal winter each year in

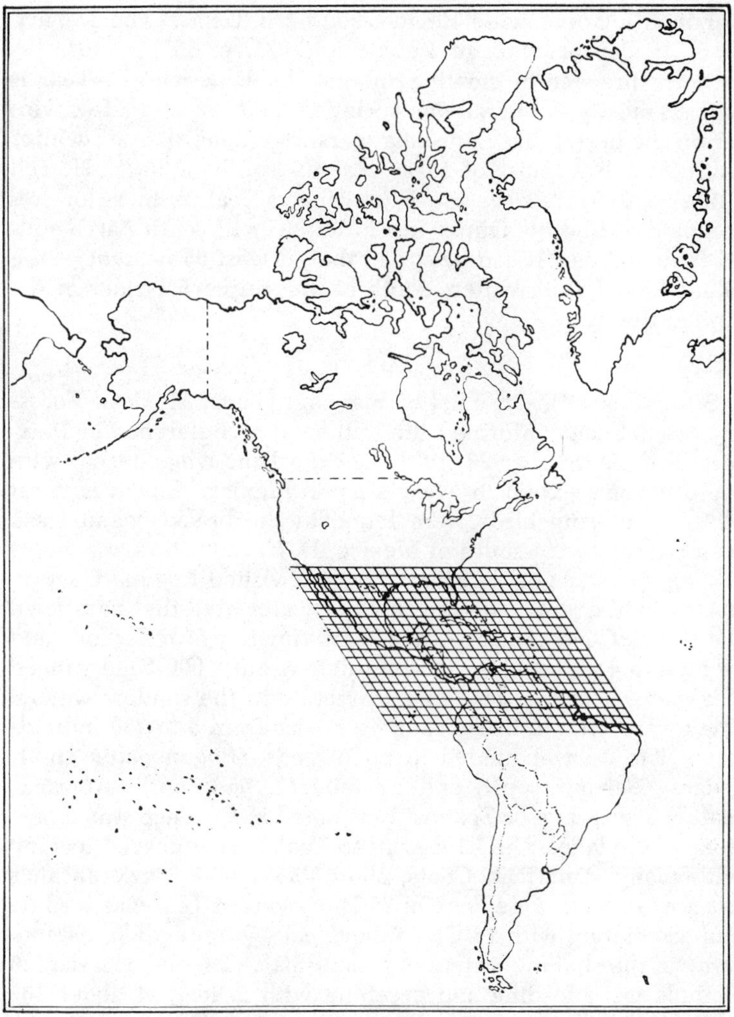

Fig. 7. The Western Hemisphere, main wintering grounds of the Blue-winged Teal.

Louisiana, but not abundantly. Mr. C. E. Gillham, of the United States Bureau of Biological Survey, who checked wintering ducks on the western Gulf Coast of the United States in the winter of 1935-36, recorded only three Blue-winged Teal. Griscom (1925) lists the Blue-winged Teal as a rare winter visitor in the Brownsville Region, southern Texas. The Department of Conservation of Louisana (1931, p. 151) states: "A summer breeder in small numbers, the Blue-winged Teal is with us mostly in the fall and spring of the year, and a few winter on the hospitable Louisiana marshes during the mid-winter cold snaps, for most of these teal fly south of us." Howell (1932, p. 140) records the Blue-winged Teal as more or less common during the winter in Florida over the entire area suited to its habits. It can be stated that at least 95 percent of the Blue-winged Teal winters south of the southern border of the United States.

MEXICO

Senor Juan Zinser, chief of Fish and Game, Mexican Forestry Department, informed the author at a conference in Mexico, D. F., December 22, 1936, that the Blue-winged Teal wintered to some extent in every state in Mexico. However, most of the wintering birds were found in the brackish and fresh water areas to the south of Mexico, D. F.

On December 29, 1936, the author visited Laguna Coyuca, State of Guerrero. This was a fresh water area that paralleled the Pacific Coast. The area was approximately 50 miles long and ½ mile to 4 miles wide. On that date about 3,000 Blue-winged Teal were observed feeding and resting in the shallow waters. They were seen in flocks ranging in size from 5 to 250 individuals. The area abounded in pondweeds (*Potamogeton* spp.), sedges (*Scirpus* spp.), and cat-tails (*Typha* spp.). Approximately 20,000 Lesser Scaups were noted in the deep water portions of the lake. The Blue-winged Teal were observed feeding with many American Coots, shore birds and Black Jacanas (*Jacana nigra*). One flock of 25 Blue-winged Teal was feeding and associating with 14 Cinnamon Teal (*Querquedula cyanoptera*) in the shallow waters of a small bay. On one occasion 26 Pintails were feeding and preening with a flock of about 100 Blue-winged Teal.

On December 30, 1936, Laguna Tres Palos, State of Guerrero, was visited. This was a brackish body of water 4 miles wide and 15 miles long, with excellent marshes occupying about one-fourth of the lake. Many small mangrove-bordered marshes adjoined the lake proper (fig. 8). Approximately 5,000 Blue-winged Teal were recorded on or near that lake. On the same trip 3,000 Widgeons, 6,000 American Coots, 1,000 Black-bellied Tree Ducks (*Dendrocygna autumnalis autumnalis*), and

1,500 Black Jacanas were observed associating with the Blue-winged Teal in shallow waters. On the deep open waters of the lake approximately 30,000 Lesser Scaups and 500 Ruddy Ducks were seen.

Crocodiles *(Crocodylus acutus)*[1] were present in both the Coyuca and Tres Palos areas. The Mexicans maintained that these reptiles were too sluggish to catch the ducks. Marsh Hawks *(Circus hudsonius)* and Caracaras *(Milvago chimachima)* were common around both lakes, but as the ducks showed but little alarm at their opproach it is doubtful if they preyed upon them.

The Valley of Mexico and Toluca Valley at one time contained many great marshes. Those marshes were drained years ago and all that is left are a few isolated lakes and numerous remnants. Of that group, Lake Texcoco, Lake Toluca and Lake Apam were visited the first week in January, 1937. Many pintails, Cinnamon Teal, Lesser Scaups, Canvas-backs and a few Redheads were observed but no Blue-winged Teal were recorded. Local sportsmen informed the author that the Blue-winged Teal became common in the interior valleys during the latter half of January. They were of the opinion that the birds worked slowly down from the north and did not arrive that far south until the latter part of January. However, our own observations of thousands of teal to the south of Mexico City on Pacific Coast lagoons indicated that the birds are on their way north when they visit the Valley of Mexico and the Toluca Valley in January. It may be that the greater part of the fall flight follows the Gulf Coast to southern Mexico and Central America, where some of the birds cross over to the Pacific Ocean and then work north and later cross over to the Gulf on the spring flight, traversing the Valleys of Mexico and Toluca in January. Such a movement would explain the influx of teal into those interior water areas.

Waterfowl were being hunted on all water areas visited in December, 1936, and January, 1937. In the isolated regions practically all shooting was done by peons. Many of the lakes were shot as heavily as some of the marshes in Iowa. The fowling pieces of the peons were of obsolete design and make. Only muzzle loaders were seen being used by the natives. The use and popularity of the muzzle loader can be explained very

[1] The scientific vertebrate animal names other than those of birds were taken from Pratt's *Manual of Vertebrates of the United States,* second edition, 1935.

FIG 8. Laguna Tres Palos, Guerrero, Mexico. A favorite wintering area.

easily. Factory manufactured 12-gauge shotgun shells cost about 16 pesos ($4.48) per box of 25 shells. The peons earn perhaps 10 to 50 centavos per day, some days. The cost is prohibitive to the peons, luckily for the ducks.

A number of peons were checked after a day's hunt to ascertain the number of ducks they were capable of taking. In most cases the bag contained less than five birds. Two or three American Coots and two or three ducks usually represented a typical bag. The poor quality of firearms and lack of shooting skill net the individual peon but few ducks. Consequently, the number of waterfowl shot yearly is not relatively so high as in our nation in which all sportsmen afford more efficient fowling pieces.

American sportsmen and upper class Mexican sportsmen are few in number compared with the number of peon hunters. With modern guns and ammunition the wealthier class of hunters have excellent sport. If the peon could afford modern breech-loading guns it is doubtful whether our southern migrating ducks would exist very long as game birds. The sportsmen of the United States have been fortunate because of the fates of the Mexican peon.

Ducks, shorebirds and doves are sold in many markets in Mexico (fig. 9). Ducks and other game are gathered from the peons and carried to the markets of the nearest towns. In Mexico City ducks may be purchased at the city markets throughout the winter. The author estimated that about 1,000 North American ducks were sold in the markets in Mexico City the first week of January, 1937. Of that number about 250 were Blue-winged Teal. The price of teal ranged from 40 to 50 centavos (12 to 14 cents) each. Pintails and Shovellers sold at two for one peso and 25 centavos (35 cents). Wilson's Snipe *(Capella delicata)* sold for 25 centavos (7 cents). Sixteen Blue-winged Teal were purchased in the market for the preparation of museum skins. Eight had been shot (one had been shot with bolt nuts) and the others had evidently been trapped as there were no shot holes present in their bodies and their necks had been broken.

It would be unfair to say nothing in favor of the Mexican game officials after giving an account of the taking of waterfowl in their country. At the present time, Juan Zinser and Daniel Gallicia, of the Forestry Department, are carrying out a sound waterfowl refuge program. Some excellent waterfowl areas are in the act of being purchased for refuges. Other areas will be acquired in the near future. The sale and utilization of game animals for a livelihood has gone on in Mexico for centuries. Age-old customs cannot be eliminated by laws in the short space of a year or two. The Mexican game officials assured us that gradually the marketing of ducks would be stopped. When a country has millions of people in destitution of the most extreme type it is not difficult for a government to let them earn a living at any occupation that does not affect their morale and health.

GUATEMALA, BRITISH HONDURAS, HONDURAS, COSTA RICA AND NICARAGUA

The Blue-winged Teal has been recorded a number of times in these countries (Phillips, 1923, p. 377-378).

PANAMA

Sturgis (1928, p. 96) stated that the Blue-winged Teal is the most common winter visitor of North American waterfowl.

FIG 9. Blue-winged Teal for sale in Latrans Market, Mexico City, December 29, 1936.

COLOMBIA

Chapman (1917, p. 233) stated: "Not uncommon at Juanchito near Cali, generally associating with the Cinnamon Teal."

ECUADOR

Chapman (1926, p. 211) recorded the Blue-winged Teal as wintering in Ecuador from the Tropical to the Temperate Zone.

VENEZUELA

Osgood and Conover (1922) stated the following concerning the bird in northwestern Venezuela: "On the first of March a flock of about twenty Blue-winged Teal was seen on a small cienega near the Rio Cogollo. . . . Later while in Merida, we were shown about ten live Q. discors, which had been trapped on a small pond near the edge of the town. The owner stated that these teal were found in that vicinity every winter, which seems peculiar, as the country is not suited to waterfowl, its only water being a swift mountain stream, and perhaps one or two artificial ponds."

ISLAND OF TRINIDAD

Chapman (1894) recorded the Blue-winged Teal as being a winter visitor of the Island of Trinidad.

BRAZIL

Naumburg (1926) stated that the Blue-winged Teal winters in Brazil and Ecuador.

CHILE

Schalow (1898) recorded the Blue-winged Teal at Ovalle, Chile. Apparently this is the southernmost record for the bird.

PERU

Phillips (1923) stated that the British Museum has a specimen of the Blue-winged Teal from Lima, Peru.

BRITISH GUIANA

Chubb (1916) recorded the Blue-winged Teal in British Guiana.

DUTCH GUIANA

Penard and Penard (1908-10) recorded the bird as being common in Dutch Guiana in November and December.

FRENCH GUIANA

Hans von Berlepsch (1908) recorded the Blue-winged Teal for French Guiana (Phillips, 1923, p. 378).

GALAPAGOS ISLANDS

Murphy (1936, p. 303) stated as follows: "The Galapagos are visited regularly by a number of migrants from the north. So far there has been recorded one duck (the Blue-winged Teal). Some of the waders clearly come south over the Pacific; the Bobolink certainly, the Blue-winged Teal probably—both are species of the Mississippi Valley—travel due south over Mexico on a line that, continued, brings them to the Galapagos."

BERMUDA ISLANDS

Bradlee, Mawbray and Eaton (1931, p. 303) had the following statement concerning the Blue-winged Teal in Bermuda: "This is a regular autumn visitor, sometimes in considerable numbers, but is irregular in its visits on the spring migration." October is given as the month of fall arrival and March as the month of spring migration.

BAHAMA ISLANDS

Cory (1890, p. 186) stated that the Blue-winged Teal is quite abundant on several of the larger islands. It is found with flocks of waterfowl frequenting creeks and ponds.

JAMAICA

Scott (1891, p. 363) recorded the Blue-winged Teal as an abundant winter visitor.

CARRIACOU ISLAND

Wells (1902, p. 243) stated: "This little duck arrives in September and October, and flocks of 10 to 20 may be seen in the mangrove swamps; they afford good sport and are in fine condition in the months of February and March. A few of them remain all year, but I have no authentic account of these breeding here."

BARBADOS ISLAND

Feilden (1889, p. 500) recorded the following: "An annual visitor in considerable numbers, generally arriving about the first week in October, and continuing to do so at intervals till Christmas.'

HAITI AND THE DOMINICAN REPUBLIC

Wetmore and Swales (1931, pp. 103-4) give the following account of the Blue-winged Teal in Haiti and the Dominican Republic: "Winter visitor, common; migrant from North America. For a bird that is reported as common there are comparatively few definite records for the Blue-winged Teal, probably because most of the specimens shot have found their way into the cooking pot. Moreau de Saint-Mery wrote that 'ducks, teals fly in clouds particularly in the Bay of Mancenialla and that of Cosbeck', a statement that must refer in part to the present bird since it is the most common of migrant ducks in the West Indies. Salle recorded it in the marshes near Higuey, Dominican Republic, and Christy shot several in the Yuna swamps but did not find it common. Verrill makes only a general statement regarding it. Abbott reported a small flock on Lake Enriquillo, October 1 to 6, 1919.

"In Haiti, Bartsch recorded the Blue-winged Teal at Glore on the Etang Saumatre April 3, 1917, and at Trou Caiman, April 4. Abbott collected one from a large flock at Les Basses on January 4, 1918, and others at the Etang Saumatre April 10 and 13, 1920.

"Saint-Mery reports teal, apparently this species from Etang Miragoane, and Descourtilz gives a very good description of the Blue-winged Teal under the name 'Sarcelle commune de Saint-Domingue.' The latter author speaks of ten species of ducks that are recognized by hunters in Haiti, and says that at Etable (near the Artibonite) ducks were so numerous that their noise disturbed his sleep. His servant in four shots at night killed fifty-eight. Officers of the Marine Corps who hunted extensively in the marshes and lakes of the lowlands informed Wetmore that from November to March this teal was the most abundant duck that they encountered and that at times it occurred in large numbers. Beebe in 1927 saw four at Source Matelas January 13 and eight March 21. He reports that he saw fifty-three killed March 2, and that the last were noted April 12. Bond found it at the Etang Miragoane, Trou Caiman and Port-de-Raix and says that it is by far the most abundant of the migrant ducks.

"This teal is one of the important game-birds of Hispaniola as its hunting is excellent sport and its flesh is palatable for the table."

PUERTO RICO

Dr. Stuart T. Danforth, professor of zoology and entomology, University of Puerto Rico, supplied the author through correspondence under date of November 11, 1936, the following information concerning the Blue-winged Teal in Puerto Rico.

Migration: Earliest fall arrivals: 30, Sept. 6, 1924; 1, Sept.

25, 1926; 14, Sept. 22, 1928; and 2, Aug. 27, 1932. Arrival of main fall flight: October 20-30. Departure of main spring flight: April 15-20. Late spring record: 3, May 2, 1924.

The greatest number observed in a single day was 2,500 on January 25 at Guanica Lagoon. Usually 200 to 350 birds was a good numbr to observe per day at Cartagena, Anagado or Guanica Lagoons from October to April.

Type of water areas frequented during winter visit. The Blue-winged Teal for the greater part frequent fresh water lagoons and generally keep to the shelter of cat-tails and sedges. The destruction of cat-tails by hurricanes and the harvesting of them by natives for roof thatching have probably lessened the numbers of teal wintering there in recent years. On Vieques Island the birds were observed quite frequently in small open pools in the midst of dense mangrove swamps in salt or brackish water.

Food habits: Only a few birds were collected and they had eaten mostly seeds, among which those of knotweed *(Persicaria portoricensis)* were very common.

Hunting: Birds are not sold in the market in Puerto Rico. Many sportsmen and would-be sportsmen take large bags of teal and other waterfowl. Often by working in groups the shooters practically eliminate the ducks on a lagoon in one afternoon, getting as many as 300 a hunt. (Danforth did not state in his letter whether this was a general practice.)

Predators: Predatory animals were not observed directly preying upon teal. The mongoose *(Herpestes birmanicus)* prowls in the outskirts of the marshes and it was observed taking American Coots, Gallinules and Ruddy Ducks. It would not be surprising to learn that this predator preys upon the Blue-winged Teal in Puerto Rico. Duck Hawks *(Falco peregrinus anatum)* occur sparingly in winter. They were seen taking other waterfowl but none was observed preying upon teal.

CUBA

Barbour (1923, p. 36) stated the following concerning the Blue-winged Teal in Cuba: "The most abundant migrant duck; it arrives in Cuba in early September and appears there often in great hosts, coming at evening to the fresh-water ponds. The day probably is spent about the inaccessible mangrove swamps of the coast. None is known to stay and nest."

LESSER ANTILLES

Cory (1898, p. 64) considered the Blue-winged Teal abundant throughout the Antilles.

EXTRALIMITAL MIGRATORY RANGE

Phillips (1923, p. 378) stated the following concerning the occurrence of the bird away from the Western Hemisphere: "This species is known to have straggled several times to western Europe. A specimen was taken in Dumfries-shire, Scotland, in January, 1858 or 1863 or both; another in Cheshire, England, 1860; a third at Ballycotton, County Cork, Ireland, September, 1910, and possibly a fourth in Cambridgeshire (British Ornith. Union Check-list). Degland and Gerde recorded a specimen for Normandy, which was probably the same one recorded by van Schauberg as having been taken on the Straits of Dover in 1957. Another specimen was taken on October 24, 1899, at Dokkum, Province of Friesland, Holland (van Oort, 1922), and there is also a record for Denmark, at Saby, northeastern Jylland, April, 1886 (Winge, 1888)."

CHAPTER V

Spring Migration

In 1937 the Blue-winged Teal in southern Mexico started northward during the early days of January. The spring flight movements, like those of the fall flight, were leisurely. When the birds got as far north as the United States, late winter storms sometimes caused alternating retreats and advances. The ducks moved slowly up the flyways with the advance of mild weather. With few exceptions, the flyways over which these birds passed were those used during the fall migration.

By the time the State of Iowa was reached many of the teal were mated and the others were in the act of courting and mating. The migrating flocks usually consisted of less than 30 birds; flocks of over 30 birds were rarely seen. It was common to see two or three pairs and single pairs migrating together. The early arrivals in Iowa were often forced to limit their resting and feeding to drainage ditches and rivers, as those were the first water areas to become free of ice in the spring. Occasionally after the lakes and marshes became free of ice a delayed cold period froze them over again and forced the early migrants back to the rivers and drainage ditches.

As a result of the spring rains and thaws in Iowa throughout March and April (1932 to 1936), thousands of cornfields were dotted with small water areas. The waste shelled corn from the previous husking season along with many weed seeds made feeding conditions ideal for migrating waterfowl.

During the past five years the ice ordinarily has gone out of the Iowa lakes and marshes during the last two weeks in March. The old time spring duck hunters in the days gone by always planned to be in the lake region on March 20 for the beginning of the spring flight of ducks. Over a period of years they had learned through trial and error that that date was usually the logical time to plan on inaugurating the spring shooting season. Mr. Lyle Van Vleck, of Ruthven, Iowa, a conductor on the Burlington Railroad until about 1906, related to the author many accounts of trains carrying duck hunters to the marshes in northwestern Iowa for the spring shooting season. Those excursions went on throughout the migration period. Spirit Lake, Ruthven, Wallingford and Lake Mills were favorite ducking locations. Many of those trains came from Chicago, Ill., and points farther east.

The activities of market hunters in those days led to the construction of freezing and packing stations throughout northern Iowa for the proper handling of ducks, shore birds and Greater Prairie Chickens *(Tympanuchus cupido americanus)*. Those birds were frozen, packed in barrels and shipped out by the boxcar load to the Chicago and New York markets. In 1900 a brace of Blue-winged Teal sold for 40 cents in the market places of the eastern cities. Although the Redhead, Canvas-back, Mallard and Pintail were the species most desired by market hunters, Blue-winged Teal were taken when the others were not available, particularly in late spring after the main flights of the other ducks had taken them on to the North.

In general the main Blue-winged Teal flight passed through the southern states between March 15 and April 15, 1932-36. The main flight arrived in the northern states between April 1 and April 30, and the flight usually arrived in Iowa between April 5 and April 15. The teal flight made its appearance in Iowa just after the main flight of the other ducks moved northward. However, as during the fall flight, the Blue-winged Teal were observed sharing the same waters with Shovellers, Pintails, Mallards, Lesser Scaup, Widgeon, Gadwalls, Green-winged Teal, Redheads, American Coots, Pied-billed Grebes and shore birds.

Because there was very little shooting (only illegal) in the United States during the spring flight, the Blue-winged Teal became very tame toward human beings on the trip to the breeding grounds. Roadside ditches, barnyard ponds and lakes inhabited by hundreds of fishermen seemed to arouse but little anxiety in them during their periods of resting, courting and feeding. Their reactions during the fall flight were entirely different, brought about by necessity.

The speed of flight, duration of flight, flying hours and height of flight were essentially the same as during the fall migration. One difference between the spring and fall flights was the courtship carried on during the spring migration. When the birds were resting and feeding between hops there was much courting. As the birds neared the nesting grounds the courtship became more ardent and there was much chasing in the air and on the water during feeding and resting periods, which is often mistaken for typical flying habits throughout the spring flight.

Bent (1923, p. 111) quoted York (1899) concerning three distinct spring flights: "The first issue of this, our tenderest, duck arrives in latitude 37° from March 25 to April 1, staying about six or eight days. The second follows a few days after the first has departed northward, up to and past the boundary line. A short period elapses when they likewise travel north to the southern part of Minnesota and its parallel. The third soon follows, and stays an indefinite period, working up through Illinois, Indiana, Wisconsin, and eastward about the last week in April if the weather permits, the Ohio, Missouri and Mississippi, with their tributaries, furnishing the flyways." The author did not observe any spring migration of the Blue-winged Teal that resembled three separate flights. The migrating population usually began with a few early birds, built up to a maximum, and then receded with the passing of the birds on to the North. True, there were variations in numbers of birds from day to day but there were no distinct separations in the spring migration.

CHAPTER VI

Courtship and Mating

Late in December, 1936, and early in January, 1937, a restlessness became apparent among the Blue-winged Teal on the wintering grounds. That uneasiness was probably a combination of the migratory and mating impulses as the attraction of males to females began at approximately the time the first signs of nuptial plumage became evident in the males. On December 30, 1936, while observing waterfowl on Laguna Coyuca, Guerrero, Mexico, Mr. C. E. Gillham and the author observed a male Blue-winged Teal bowing and swimming around a female at the edge of a lily bed. The following day at Laguna Tres Palos in the same state the author recorded two males mildly bowing and dipping before a lone female in a mangrove swamp. The nuptial plumage of the males was barely noticeable on those dates.

Mating activities became much more evident as spring advanced. By the end of March, when the first birds reached Iowa, the process of courting had become a daily affair. As the sex ratio was about 1.5 males to 1 female there were many females that had more than one male in attendance. When there was more than one male, the female seemed to pay about as much attention to one as the other at that period of the spring. The males attempted to chase each other away from the female time after time but success was rarely achieved early in the flight. In some cases the female chased away a male, but he soon returned and she showed no particular animosity toward him, even going so far as to drive away his rival.

By the middle of April, when the main flight passes through Iowa, the mating season was more ardent than among the first migrating birds seen in March. It seemed that, although the courtship began in December and January, the closer the nesting season approached the more intense the mating became.

Many females were courted by one to four males, but usually when not in pairs the number most commonly seen together was two males and one female. Thompson (1890) observed just the opposite of this, "I have frequently remarked that during the breeding season this species may be seen coursing over and around the pond in threes, and these when shot usually prove a male and two females."

Bent (1925, p. 112) stated that the courtship of the Blue-winged Teal was largely performed on the wing. As courtship occurred largely during the migration period it could be expected that part of the courtship would be carried out in the air. The author observed much coursing and dipping over the waterways between the main flights, and part of those flight demonstrations were surely nuptial activities. However, the most interesting phase of the courtship took place on the water and along the beaches or mud flats. By crawling quietly through the grasses up to the edge of a pothole the author often observed the courtship and mating routine taking place on the water and along the shore. The males and females, or male and female swam slowly about, bowing to each other. Many times that bowing took place in unison. On other occasions either the male or the female bowed singly for a time without the other apparently paying any attention. The head and neck of the bowing birds went up and down and slightly outward. As many as 31 bows per minute were recorded for several minutes at a time. The swimming around each other and bowing took place for hours at a time, interrupted with feeding and resting periods. At times one male chased another male away from the female. Prior to the chasing, both males and the female often courted for hours before dissension arose. After several days of persistent chasing one or the other finally emerged the victor. Often while flying the males uttered peep-like whistles, but were never heard to quack. The greater part of the courtship periods occurred from daylight to 10 a. m. and from 4 p. m. to dark. In Iowa by May 10 (about two weeks prior to the peak of the nesting season) there was only one male to each female. Furniss (1935) stated that the sex ratio of the Blue-winged Teal in the breeding grounds of Manitoba was 1.5 males to 1 female. As all of the author's sex ratio records indicated a balanced sex ratio during the nesting season in Iowa, the unmated males evidently moved on northward finally to spend the summer at the northern part of their range as unmated birds.

COPULATION

Before a female definitely paired with one particular male it was not uncommon to see two or three males in attendance trying to copulate with the female. On at least two occasions the author observed with certainty the treading of one female by two males. By the time the nesting season actually began there was only one male to each female and they were definitely mated.

The act of copulation was a climax in courtship display on the part of both female and male. The birds swam or walked around each other bowing, and finally the male swam directly toward the female. The female usually swam rapidly away but was soon overtaken, whereupon the male covered her and reached out with his bill and grasped her by the back of the head. During nuptial water chase the female swam low in the water with her neck stretched far out in front, the neck, chin and lower mandible skimming the water. When the male covered the female, copulation took place. The struggle was so intense that the female was often pushed completely under the water for several seconds. The time taken for copulation averaged about 10 seconds. After the act was completed both birds swam around, serenely preening themselves or merely resting quietly in the water.

COMBATIVENESS WITH OTHER SPECIES

For the most part the Blue-winged Teal did very little combating with other species at any time. During the month of May, American Coots were observed chasing teal away from certain areas in the marshes. However, the combats were of short duration and apparently settled no question. A typical combat was for a coot, or sometimes two or three coots, to drive a pair of teal from their immediate vicinity. Often the ducks swam back among the coots in a few minutes. No teal were observed to be evicted from a desirable nesting area by the coots.

CHAPTER VII

Nesting

The first indications that teal were going to nest was evident by their attraction to certain water areas. There were many inspections made of all types of water areas as a preliminary step in establishing a certain area for the home base. Apparently both female and male flew over the area many times inspecting potholes, sloughs and marshes. The birds alighted on those water areas and it seemed as though they actually inspected them carefully. Many times, pairs were observed to alight on a pothole and slowly waddle around the margin as if trying to determine if the area was suitable.

After a water area had been chosen both the female and the male were observed walking out into the grassy upland as though they were seeking a nest site. What part the male played in choosing the nest site would be difficult to say. He may have merely followed the female because of his attraction to her. However, as the time approached for the construction of the nest the male had nothing to do with the picking of the nest site or the construction of the nest. The nesting site was chosen without any interference on the part of the male. The female flew over the surrounding upland and dropped to the ground. If the male was flying with her, he returned to the water area. Once the female was on the ground she walked and sneaked along inspecting clumps of grasses and other places in which to build her nest.

There were preliminary attempts at nest building which were soon abandoned. At the beginning of the duck studies in 1932 the author found many depressions scooped out of the

FIG. 10. A typical Blue-winged Teal nest in bluegrass cover.

earth in clumps of grasses and weeds that were about six inches in diameter and one-half to an inch in depth. It was later found that these depressions were the first attempts at nest building. Several females were caught in the act of scooping out these depressions with their feet. The dew of early morning aided them greatly in softening the soil to scrape it.

It was not determined how many false attempts were made before a nest was actually completed. In each case where the author flushed a bird from her preliminary work she never returned to finish the task. Perhaps if a female was frightened by some animal during the nest building procedure she likewise abandoned the work and went elsewhere.

THE NEST

After the nesting site had been chosen came the task of building the nest. Whether the nest was built in a rolling bluegrass pasture (fig. 10), in an alfalfa field, in a bog, spotted with hillocks grown up to slough grass, or on a muskrat house, there was always a slight depression scraped out of the soil to fit the base of the nest. Dead grasses and other dead vegetation of the previous year were tucked into the hollow and by much picking and assorting they were matted loosely together to form the bowl of the nest. After the grassy lining of the nest had been arranged, the sides of the grassy bowl were lined with down. The bottom of the nest contained but a small amount of down. Most of the down was placed around the rim of the nest. The fluffy down feathers formed a loose batting intermixed with the grasses that may be easily pulled over the eggs to hide them from ever alert eyes. The downy covering also probably helped to maintain a more constant egg temperature when the female was away from the nest.

The grasses and down together were about three inches in thickness at the rim of the nest. This fluffy rim could be pulled over the eggs in a few seconds at the approach of danger or when the female left the nest on her own accord to exercise and feed. The 415 nests observed in Iowa, South Dakota and Minneosta averaged 7 to 10 inches in diameter from the outside edge and 4 to 6 inches in depth.

DOWN FEATHERS

The down feathers, plucked from the breast of the female, resemble in texture small fluffy balls of cotton (fig. 11). Each little ball of down is one feather. The base of the many fine plumes is of a dull white color graduating into a light brown-gray color toward the end.

ELEVATION OF NESTS

The greatest proportion of nests under observation were situated in dry habitats. Two percent of the nests was constructed in water or on damp soil recently flooded. Ninety-eight percent of the nests was definitely on well-drained soil at the time of nest building. The average elevation above the marsh level of the total number of nests was 2.4 feet. The extremes were: one nest located in one-half inch of water, and one nest built on the top of a hay stack with an elevation of 25 feet.

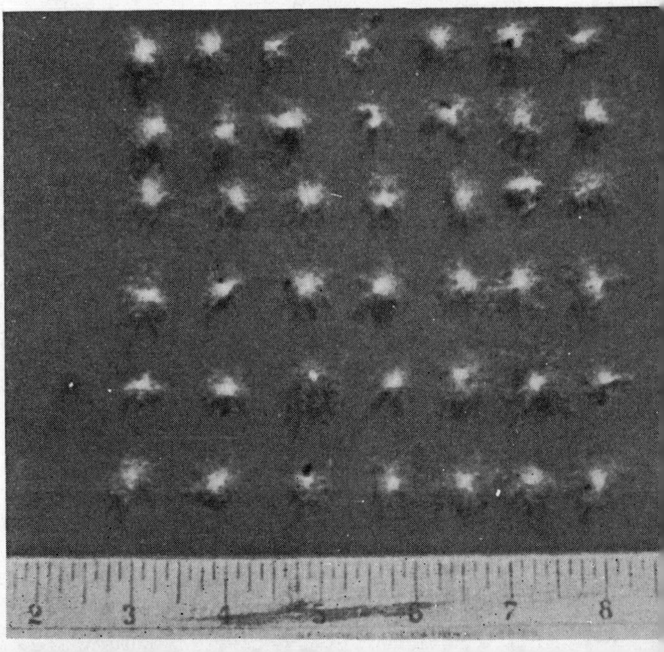

FIG. 11. Down feathers as found in nests.

FIG. 12. One egg eaten by striped skunk within three inches of nest. The eggs in the nest were not disturbed.

DISTANCE OF NESTS FROM WATER

Nest sites were found in water and as far away as one mile from water. The average distance from water was 41.5 yards. The two extremes were: nests found in water and two nests found one mile from any water. It was found that 95.6 percent of the nests was located within 220 yards of the shoreline.

EGG LAYING

Egg laying actually began in many cases before the nests were constructed. Each spring from April 15 to May 15 single eggs were found on lake shores, in fields and in pastures where they had been dropped promiscuously. Many of those eggs were deposited in the open where they were easily found by other animals. Such eggs were soon destroyed and, because of the conspicuousness of such destruction, many casual observers assumed that they represented destroyed nests. The dropping of eggs in coverless areas may teach certain animals the egg-eating habit and lead to nest destruction later.

There was evidence that many of the late-arriving females were ready for egg deposition upon their arrival in Iowa. Just how many eggs were layed prior to the actual deposition in nests was not learned, nor what effect preliminary laying had upon the final number of eggs per clutch. Stoddard (1931, p. 28) considered single dropped eggs of the Eastern Bob-white *(Colinus virginianus virginianus)* an indication of nest destruction, the egg dropped before another attempt at renesting.

Nest building appeared to be rushed in some instances because the female was in condition for laying. In 12 nests just started, single eggs were found in the hollowed-out depressions of the soil. Each egg was quite muddy or soil-stained, brought about by the female's completing the scooping of the nest base after the egg had been laid.

After the nest had been lined with dead grasses and down, and egg laying had become a routine, eggs were seldom found outside of the nest. On six occasions single eggs were found three inches to three feet from a nest. Whether those eggs were deposited as the female was frightened off the nest or were deposited on the way to the nest was not determined. Often the ill-deposited eggs were eaten by other animals (fig. 12).

Once egg laying had started one egg was deposited in the nest each day until the clutch was completed. Egg laying usually took place in the morning between 7 a. m. and 11 a. m. Each day after the egg had been layed the female covered the egg or eggs and flew to the waiting male on the marsh or pothole. On the return to the nest the next day the male accompanied the female, both flying very low over the prairie. When the female came in the vicinity of the nest, she dropped suddenly to the earth; but the male did not slacken his flight in the least as he kept on flying and returned to the pothole. This act was one of camouflage, whether intentional or not. It took a quick eye to realize, from several hundred yards, that the female was down. The closest that a female was observed alighting near a nest was 20 yards. Often she dropped to the ground as far as 200 yards from the nest. After alighting she sneaked through the grasses and weeds to the nest, and it was impossible at times to see her approach the nest from where she alighted. Approximately 90 percent of the nests had complete clutches of eggs by the end of the last week in May.

During the egg-laying period and the early days of incubation the male waited for the female on some nearby marsh or pothole. Favorite waiting spots were the tops of muskrat *(Ondatra zibethica)* houses and the tops of glacial boulders

FIG. 13. *(left)* A glacial boulder that was used as a waiting site by a male Blue-winged Teal. FIG. 14. *(right)* An old rotted down muskrat house that was used as a male waiting site. (Photos by H. H. Knight.)

FIG. 15. *(left)* The female was frightened from this nest. Note the defecation on the eggs. (Photo by H. H. Knight.) FIG. 16. *(right)* Blue-winged Teal ducklings from one minute to two hours old. (Photo by Herb Schwartz.)

that may be found in some of the water areas of Iowa (figs. 13 and 14). However, many water areas had neither muskrat houses nor boulders for perching sites, and the males were found standing or sitting hour after hour along the shores. In one case the horizontal limb of a willow (*Salix* sp.) two feet above the water was utilized as a waiting site.

Several times upon approaching a pothole during the early part of the nesting season the author observed males sneaking off through the bulrushes in the opposite direction. By swimming quietly and with head and neck stretched out just skimming the surface of the water they soon disappeared. Tramping and searching failed to flush them in some instances. One afternoon during the early days of the nesting season of 1936 Dr. George O. Hendrickson and the author spent one hour beating out a one-quarter acre pothole in order to flush a male that had eluded him in the above manner. The bird was not found although a thorough search was made.

Occasionally a male would be so enamored of a female that, when an observer approached, he flew around in low circles over the area in which she was building a nest or depositing an egg. The male's action may have been of a warning nature. It was not a common occurrence, as it was only noted a few times during the course of the studies.

A total of 341 normal nests were recorded in Iowa, South Dakota, North Dakota and Minnesota with a total of 3,171 eggs, averaging 9.3 eggs per nest. The smallest number of eggs was

6 and the largest number, 14. The eggs were of a light buff-tan color and varied but little in shades. The shell was very smooth and slightly glossy, more so as incubation progressed from the close contact of the duck's abdomen. Bent (1923, p. 114) stated the following concerning the size of the eggs: "The measurements of 93 eggs in various collections average 46.6 by 33.4 millimeters; the eggs showing the four extremes measure 49.5 by 35, 47.2 by 36.2, 43.5 by 32, and 45.6 by 31.3 millimeters." Of the 3,171 eggs observed by the author there was not one with a deformed shell.

What factors determined the number of eggs per clutch was not learned. The size of the nest may be a factor in determining the number of eggs that will be layed in the nest. It was found that 4.7 percent of the Blue-winged Teal nests was parasitized by the Ring-necked Pheasant *(Phasianus colchicus torquatus)*. In the parasitized nests the number of pheasant eggs lowered the number of duck eggs deposited in the nest. When a nest became filled with eggs, laying ceased and incubation began. This observation led the author to believe that perhaps the size of the nest may determine the number of eggs that will be deposited.

The number of eggs deposited in renesting attempts averaged much smaller than in initial attempts. Twenty-seven nests (renesting attempts) averaged only 4.3 eggs to the nest.

INCUBATION

Incubation began within 24 hours after the last egg had been layed. The female left the nest for exercise, rest and feeding purposes once or twice each day. Usually the rest periods were about 7 a. m. and 7 p. m. The females were observed to stay away from the nest 20 minutes to 2 hours. Occasionally females were seen to leave the nest during the middle

FIG. 17. Caps of eggs left in nest after young had hatched.

of the day. On those brief trips back to feed and rest she returned to the waiting male. After about the third day of incubation the attraction of the male for the female apparently waned, and in a few days he flew away to other water areas to accompany males in the same category. The flocks of males varied in numbers from 3 to 35 individuals. These flocks moved around quite frequently from one water area to another and as a rule did not associate with the brood females or young until the latter part of the rearing season.

Upon leaving the nest of her own accord the female always covered the eggs very carefully with down. Each day a small amount of down was added to the downy covering. By the time the incubation date arrived the maximum amount of down had been deposited in the rim of the nest. The down was pulled over the eggs by a shuffling of the feet aided by pulling and plucking with the bill.

In the early stages of incubation the female flushed from the nest when frightened and flew directly away without a great deal of fuss. After several days of incubation she uttered low quacks and flew in circles for a short time about the observer before flying away. Upon returning to the nest the approach was always stealthy. At times the brooding bird slipped back to the nest under the very eyes of the observer. On about 75 percent of the occasions when an incubating duck was flushed from the nest she defecated watery feces on the eggs as she flew away. The fecal matter invariably had a very strong disturbing odor. Whether this act was of a repellent nature or a fright reaction the author cannot say (fig. 15). Her attachment for the nest and eggs became increasingly apparent as the date of hatching approached. The periods of feeding became shortened. It was doubtful whether she left the nest at all the last 48 hours of incubation.

When the female was frightened from the nest during the last four days of incubation she usually fluttered off, simulating broken wings and legs and all the while uttering plaintive quacks. More attentive females were observed to walk away from the nest only a few feet and waddle around quacking in distress. When the observer came too close, she flew a short distance, alighted and continued her actions of a wounded bird. If the observer waited until she finally flew away, he had but a short time to wait until the devoted bird was back again, flying in small circles and uttering low quacks of anxiety.

HATCHING

Between 21 and 23 days after incubation began the ducklings hatched. As far as could be observed by field observations, most of the ducklings hatched within the last 12 hours of the twenty-second day. It was impossible in most cases to tell when the last egg was layed and when incubation began. During the laying period and the early days of incubation too frequent visits to the nest resulted in desertion, thus the lack of more complete data concerning the incubation period. About 80 percent of the ducklings hatched between June 16 and June 28 each year during the course of the study.

Within four hours after the first egg was pipped all of the young had hatched (except dead or weak ones). In another three or four hours the ducklings became dry. Figure 16 shows a brood of eight young almost dry and nearly ready for the trip to water. As soon as the young were dry, or shortly thereafter, the trek to the water area began. So far as could be determined, the young were taken to water within 12 hours after hatching.

Many times the young had hatched and left the nest when the author checked the nest toward the latter part of the nesting season. In nests just recently vacated the presence of egg caps indicated that the young had hatched. When the eggs were destroyed by some predator the egg fragments were not left as caps off the end of the egg. The caps (fig. 17) varied in size and shape to a certain degree but one could always see that they had been pipped off in a circular pattern.

NESTING TERRITORY

The normal nesting territory was that area within 220 yards of the water's edge. Slightly less than 5 percent of the females built nests farther than 220 yards away from water. Nests were found at the rate of 1 nest per 100 acres to 1 nest per 1/10 acre within 220 yards of a water area. At no time did the author observe females defending nesting areas.

MALE WAITING TERRITORY

The waiting sites occupied by males while the females built nests or deposited eggs represented waiting territories. The number of desirable waiting sites seemed to determine the number of males in a certain water area. Males were not observed defending or fighting over waiting sites.

CHAPTER VIII

Rearing of Young

The tribulations of the rearing season began as soon as the ducklings hatched from the egg. After the young had hatched and had become dry, the mother led them almost immediately toward the water. Many nests are located quite a distance from a suitable body of water. The farther the nest is from water the greater the hazard of the trek to the rearing ground. Where the nest was as far as one mile from water the little ducklings may have been taxed to the limit of their endurance to reach the rush-grown water. No evidence was obtained concerning the loss of young to predators or over-exertion from the nest to water.

On numerous occasions mother teal were observed escorting their downy broods across pastures, cornfields, oat stubble and across and down roads to the marshy areas. The female in leading her young did not always utilize the shortest route or the nearest water area. Grass-grown cow paths seemed to be used as lanes of travel when they were available. Such paths did not necessarily lead directly toward a marsh or pothole, for when paths angled in the general direction of the chosen water area they were used. Apparently too dense a growth of vegetation made traveling difficult. On June 24, 1933, the author observed a female and nine young cross through a patch of very rank and dense bluegrass and weeds about 50 yards wide. Twelve minutes were used in traversing the narrow strip of cover. On numerous occasions broods were led down gravel roads. In the open, such as roads, cow paths and heavily grazed pastures the birds traveled at a rate of about two miles per hour. Considering the types of cover found in the area under observation it can be stated that most of the ducklings reached the water within two hours after they left the nest.

Throughout the trip from the nest to water the mother was constantly on the watch for any danger. When approached by man the female ran or flew a short distance in a crippled manner away from the young, quacking low warning notes to the ducklings all the while. The ducklings scampered in all directions and hid in the grasses and weeds in a very few seconds. With their protective coloration they squatted under a few blades of grass and were completely hidden. The author tried to find ducklings hidden in grassy areas many times but met with only slight success. Usually when aware of such observations the adult remained but a few paces away nervously quacking and trying to lead the intruder away.

Upon reaching the water there was little or no ceremony in leading the ducklings to their first aquatic home. On June 20, 1934, 11 a. m., a female was observed leading nine young down an old cow path to Mud Lake, Clay County. Arriving at the lake the old bird made several preliminary trips up and down the water's edge and then waded in, the ducklings following as if they had been following her for days. The water area a few feet out from shore had a heavy growth of cat-tails *(Typha latifolia)* and bulrushes *(Scirpus occidentalis)*. The entire family quickly disappeared into that protective cover.

From the time the ducklings reached the water they remained the greater part of the time in dense cover or close to it until they were able to fly. The main feeding periods of the young birds were from daylight to 9 a. m. and from 5 p. m. to dark each day. During the feeding the brood was led out a short distance in open water, where most of the feeding was done around the edges of the growth of cat-tails, bulrushes and arrowheads. Open places in the marsh, such as openings cleared by muskrats, were favorite feeding places. The ducklings were also frequently seen feeding along the edges of emergent vegetation facing the large open water areas. Rarely were juveniles seen feeding far from the protection of cover.

Ducklings only a few days old were aided by their mother in the daily feeding. The young were often seen scampering over the surface of the water, uttering a weak call, between a "peep" and a "whistle," toward the mother who had found a choice morsel. The female usually yielded the food to the hun-

FIG. 18. An old rotten muskrat house grown up to smartweeds furnished ideal roosting and resting sites for young and adults.

gry young. After the birds were a week old they demanded little attention from the mother in providing food. Each little duck busily swam and scurried about retrieving food on its own accord. However, until the young were five weeks old the mother, in an expert manner, guided and led the ducklings to the more likely feeding spots. During the first five weeks the young birds swam together in a rather compact group or "block" formation. The female, by swimming near the front of the brood on either side was able to crowd or lead the young in the direction that she wished. At times the "block" of juveniles swimming close together appeared at first glance as if the moving mass were a single animal. At such times the young moved in unison, and because they camouflaged very well with vegetation, they were exceedingly difficult to observe.

The "block" formation was carried on at its greatest degree of efficiency in times of danger. At the approach of enemies the mother swiftly directed the young into nearby cover. If the enemy continued to come closer, the female flushed from the water, quacking warning and distress calls. Usually she alighted only a short distance away, trying to decoy the intruder in the opposite direction of the young. If the enemy remained, the female soon began flying in short circles, passing near the hidden ducklings. As she flew, low quacks were given; and, by watching closely, one would see the "block" of young move in unison from one clump of cover to another, away from the point of danger. The quacks of the female appeared to be a discourse to the young on how to get away from the immediate vicinity. If one rushed the group of young they scattered in every direction. By diving, swimming and scampering over the surface of the water they disappeared and it was almost impossible to locate them again that day. On one occasion the author and Dr. Paul L. Errington located a mother with a brood of eight on a pothole of one acre in size. The juveniles were about 10 days old. The cat-tails and bulrushes had been eliminated by grazing. A band of barren pasture about 50 yards wide surrounded the water. Several birds were needed for food habits study and it was decided that the birds could be collected very easily. With an insect net, the author made a dash into the pothole to obtain the specimens. The unexpected happened! The mother flew to one end of the pond and the young were chased to the other end. Fully expecting the young to be easily caught, the author was surprised when the ducklings climbed out on the shore and ran toward a cornfield 50 yards away. While the author struggled through the muck the ducklings reached the cornfield and safety. The mother remained on the pond quacking and feigning, trying to retard the intentions of capturing the young. The family was never seen on that body of water again. Presumably they moved on to another lake 440 yards away.

The mother and young made use of numerous types of resting and roosting places by day as well as night. One of the favorite roosting sites was an old rotted down muskrat house grown up to smartweeds *(Polygonum Muhlenbergii),* (fig. 18). During the rearing season the smartweeds were from 12 inches to 36 inches in height. As the tops of many old muskrat houses were but a few inches from the surface of the water they were very accessible. Houses surrounded by water were very advantageous roosting places in the event of danger. The birds were able to sneak down off the house on the side opposite the approaching enemy without creating any noise or attraction and quietly glide into other cover. Other resting and roosting sites used were muskrat feeding stations, rotten clumps of bulrushes, old American Coot nests, water-free margins grown up to cat-tails, bulrushes, phragmites or arrowheads. Those places were also used in stormy weather by the young and adults.

The juveniles grew and developed rapidly. By the time they were six weeks old they had begun to fly. The birds learned to fly during the periods of feeding early in the morning and late in the evening. While chasing each other after food, and perhaps during play and exercise, the beating wings lift them into the air as soon as they are sufficiently developed. From the time they first learn to fly their daily flights become longer and stronger. July 15 was the earliest date on which young teal were observed flying. Most of the young birds began flying each year about August 10. By August 20 some of the year's young were already migrating.

In the prairie region many potholes and sloughs went dry each year. Even in years of normal rainfall the more shallow water areas seldom held water throughout the summer. If a female had taken her brood to a shallow pothole, she had to lead the young to other waters during July or August. In many instances the young were forced to walk because they were too young to fly. Each year since 1932 the author has observed many potholes go dry about July 15, forcing ducks and ducklings to seek new homes. In most prairie marsh areas there were deeper and more permanent sloughs and marshes that withstood the dry periods of summer. No adults or ducklings were observed that had died because of the drying up of a water area in Iowa.

The drying up of the smaller water areas each year resulted in a concentration of rearing ducklings and adults in the remaining areas. On these concentration grounds there was a great deal of intermixing of broods during feeding and roosting periods. This intermixing often resulted in very large broods for some ducks and very small broods for others. One adult female was observed in 1933 with a following of 42 juveniles of varying ages. Broods of 20 to 30 individuals were seen many times. Observations led the author to believe that the young at times may follow several females in the course of a few days. When the mother of a brood died, the young apparently attached themselves to another brood without any difficulty whatsoever.

CHAPTER IX

Nest Destruction and Juvenile Mortality

In presenting these data concerning the destruction of nests and juvenile mortality factors the author is well aware that the information was obtained in an area of intensive agriculture and the findings are typical for only that part of the breeding range which is devoted almost entirely to agriculture. The greater part of the breeding range of the Blue-winged Teal, however, falls within the agricultural areas of North America.

NEST DESTRUCTION

A total of 250 Blue-winged Teal nests were observed in Iowa. Of that number 223 were normal, full-season nests. Fifty-nine and six-tenths percent (133 nests) of those nests was successful (table III). Twenty-seven renesting attempts were recorded (table IV). Only 14.8 percent (4 nests) of the renesting attempts was successful.

RENESTING ATTEMPTS

The differentiation of normal nests from renesting attempts for the most part was very difficult. The author combined three methods to differentiate normal nests from renesting attempts. The average number of eggs per renesting attempt was 4.3 compared with 9.3 eggs per normal nest. The number of eggs in a nest was correlated with the time of discovery and time of hatching or destruction. Thus, when a nest of 6 eggs was found July 5, it was assumed that the nest represented a renesting attempt. Nests constructed during the latter days of June and in July were often poorly constructed (fig. 19). The small number of eggs, date of nest building, poor cover selection, and the small amount of down in such nests left little doubt as to the status of the nest. The author knows that 75 percent of the nests (p. 122) was found. For the 90 normal nests destroyed, 27 renesting attempts were found. If the 27 renesting attempts represented 75 percent of the total renestings, there were probably about 36 (40 percent) renesting attempts for the 90 nests destroyed. Over the five-year period 14.8 percent of the renesting attempts was successful.

There was evidence that a few repeated (third or more) renesting attempts were successful under some conditions. A brood of seven young, three to four days old, was seen on

TABLE III. *History of Blue-winged Teal Nests in Iowa*

Cause of destruction	1932	1933	1934	1935	1936	Total	Percentage
Mowing	12	8	12	4	1	37	16.6
Flooding			15			15	6.8
Crows		1		3	1	5	2.2
Trampling by cattle	1	2	4	1		8	3.6
Unknown				3	1	4	1.8
Striped skunk				4	1	5	2.2
Deserted		2	1	1		4	1.8
Franklin ground squirrel				4		4	1.8
Unknown mammal				1		1	.4
Mink			1			2	.9
Burning		1	3			3	1.3
Badger					1	1	.4
Infertile eggs			1			1	.4
Completed hatching	18	58	28	22	7	133	59.6
Total	31	72	65	43	12	223	

TABLE V. *History of Renesting Attempts in Iowa*

Cause of destruction	1933	1934	1935	1936	Total	Percentage
Crows		5		2	7	25.9
Mowing		3			3	11.1
Unknown mammal		2			2	7.8
Striped skunk				1	1	3.7
Trampled by cattle		3			3	11.1
Deserted		1	2		3	11.1
Unknown		1	1		2	7.8
Badger				2	2	7.8
Completed hatching	1	0	2	1	4	14.8
Total	1	15	5	6	27	

Green Slough, Clay County, Iowa, August 19, 1936. One other brood of seven young, one week old, was seen on the same water area August 21, 1936. Those broods could have been young from the nests of exceedingly late nesting birds or, more likely, they represented the outcome of true renesting attempts. It may have been that a number of nests of each pair was destroyed one after the other before incubation had advanced enough to discourage the male birds.

From the data presented the author believes that the majority of female teal have but one good opportunity to produce a brood of young each year.

WEATHER

The abandonment and destruction of nests were brought about by a wide variety of causes, most of which were determined. The greatest cause for nest destruction other than by acts of man was unfavorable weather. During the height of the nesting season in 1934 a five-inch rain fell in several hours; 19 percent of the nests was deserted because of flooding. No abnormal periods of precipitation occurred during the nesting season in 1932, 1933, 1935 or 1936.

The disruption of nests by flooding had several aspects. Where a nest was subjected to a swift flow of water, often after the water receded no traces could be found of the nest. Where rising back water engulfed a nest the author found the eggs and nest in a mold of settled silt after the fall of the water level. Practically all flooded eggs were mud-stained. All flooded nests were deserted by the brooding females.

There was one very interesting observation made concerning a nest site during high water. On June 20, 1935, Dr. George O. Hendrickson, Charles Friley, Jr., and the author came upon a nest of eight eggs being incubated by a female situated on top of a hummock of bog in slough grass midst the waters of flood stage. With much reluctance the female flushed from the perilous nest. Upon examination of the nest it was found that the eight eggs were pipped and the ducklings were alive in the shell. The high water was about two inches below the eggs at that time. There was no down in the nest, no scooped out depression, and the tall marsh grass under the eggs was living and of a fresh green color. The absence of down and depression seemed to indicate that the eggs had been moved to safer quarters. Further, if the duck had incubated the eggs in that spot for 23 days, the grasses under the eggs would have been dead

FIG. 19. A renesting attempt. Note the small number of eggs and poor nest construction.

and would have had a brown color. Such evidence surely indicated that the eggs had been moved to the hummock a short time before. However, it is difficult to conceive how a duck could move the eggs upon a hummock that had an abrupt elevation of 12 inches. The ducklings did not hatch. They died, probably of chilling brought about by the observers' frightening the female from the nest at such a critical time.

Each year during the rearing season heavy rains were recorded. After each storm the following two or three days were spent scouring the marshes for dead or injured birds. In 1933 a severe hail and rain storm occurred during the first week of July. Within three days following the storm three dead ducklings about one week old were found, apparently having been killed by the stormy weather. On June 24, 1935, after a heavy rain, one teal duckling was found that appeared to have died from drowning. It is doubtful that many ducklings were killed by rain or hail because at the approach of a storm the mother teal quickly hustled her young to an old weed-grown muskrat house or into the heavy growths of cat-tails, flags, calamus, bulrushes or bur-reeds, where they received protection from the elements.

The severe drought years of 1934 to 1936 had few ill effects upon the ducklings in Iowa. In 1934 the drought began during the nesting season, resulting in the elimination of much nesting cover, and there were consequently fewer nests and greater nest destruction. The young that hatched made their way safely to the rearing water areas. In 1936 all of the young had hatched before the drought became noticeable, but scores of duckling-inhabited potholes and sloughs went dry before many of the young teal could fly. When water areas were nearly dry the mother teal led the young across fields and pastures to larger bodies of water. Not a single duckling was found stranded in a former water area, and none was found dead between water areas. American Coot chicks and the young of Pied-billed Grebes, however, were often found dead in their old haunts that had gone dry.

The drying up of some potholes and small marshes was usually an annual happening in the prairie area (fig. 20). Each year for the past five years many broods of young ducks were forced to trek to more favorable waters. The teal were good walkers and apparently most of them made the overland journey without a great deal of difficulty.

It is known that ducklings can be trapped in potholes and marshes that are drying up. West of Iowa, in the prairie states, where severe drought conditions have prevailed over a longer period of years, the mortality of young ducks was great in some instances. Many of the western marshes began to recede in 1930, leaving a margin of oozy mud between the remaining water and the shore. By the middle of the rearing season in 1933 the marshes gave up the last of the water, leaving only a wide margin of treacherous mud and slime. During that year large numbers of flightless ducks were forced to meet their death by starvation, thirst, engulfment by mud and predation because they could not get to protected areas.

MOWING

A large percentage of the wet-meadow acreage vegetated to slough grass was mowed each year for feeding and packing purposes (fig. 21). Although there was no set time each spring or summer for the haying harvest to begin, in most years the cutting operations began in June. Sometimes excessive rainfall and backward crops kept the harvesters out of the wild hay lands until July.

Alfalfa was usually cut the first time between June 1 and 10. In 1935 wet weather retarded the initial cutting for several weeks. The acreage of alfalfa within nesting distance of

FIG. 20. *(left)* A pothole going dry early in July. FIG. 21. *(right)* The margin of a pothole mowed to the water's edge. Mowing should be withheld until after July 1. (Photo by P. A. DuMont.)

marshes was about 100 acres. However, this small acreage supported duck nests each year.

A total of 40 nests, 16 percent, were destroyed by mowing operations. A mowed-over nest was almost invariably a failure, even though the eggs were not disturbed and the female was uninjured. About one-half of the incubating ducks deserted the nests immediately and egg-eating animals quickly found a ready meal. The lack of cover around the other 50 percent gave little or no protection to the nests with the result that they were soon destroyed by any animal that desired to eat an egg. One duck managed to bring off her brood after a mowing operation. Of the 40 mowed-over nests recorded only one duck was injured by a mower.

Many farmers raised the sickle bar when they knew a nest was present, but the "island" of vegetation left around the nest attracted a number of curious animals to the scene within a very short time, resulting in the destruction of the nest.

All of the destroyed nests were mowed over in June. No nests were revealed by mowing in July. The mowing of tall marsh grass and alfalfa was delayed until the first week in July in 1935 by almost continuous precipitation during the month of June. As a result of the rainfall very little hay was cut and about 98 percent of the teal nests located in alfalfa and tall marsh grass escaped the mowing.

BURNING

Three nests, 1.2 percent, were destroyed by fires. The burning of marshland and prairie areas during the nesting season may be incendiary (for the collection of hay insurance), spontaneous combustion, accidental (sparks from trains, cigarettes and rubbish fires out of control), lightning, for the assumed purpose of improving stands of hay, and for insect control. Conflagration at any time during May and June would destroy a large number of duck nests, as well as the nests of other game and non-game birds. The wise use of fire may be necessary in carrying out management practices but the time for its use is not during the nesting season.

DOMESTIC ANIMALS

Trampling by Cattle. Eleven nests, 4.4 percent, were demolished by cattle. The destruction of nests by trampling took place in every instance in overgrazed areas. Seven of the 11 destroyed nests were trampled in June, 1934, the year of the severe drought. The nesting cover of the marshes was greatly reduced by grass-killing heat and overgrazing, thus causing a concentration of cattle in some areas where nesting cover remained.

Dogs. The average farmer of northwestern Iowa usually had but one dog on his farm. As a rule farm dogs were not tramps. Very seldom was a dog seen roaming at large in a duck nesting area. No nests were found that had been disturbed by dogs. The author used Water Spaniel, Chesapeake and Pointer dogs to locate duck nests. Those dogs found duck nests very easily (they were trained not to touch the nest or to chase the incubating female) and their actions and ability foretold what a pack of hungry, roaming dogs could do in a nesting area.

REPTILES

Snakes. The most common snake in northwestern Iowa was the plains garter-snake *(Thamnophis radix radix)*. Eighty-five specimens of this species were captured in one afternoon, June, 1933, in one of the best teal nesting areas. No evidence was obtained that indicated any egg destruction by this snake. The red-barred garter-snake *(Thamnophis sirtalis parietalis)* and the western ribbon-snake *(Thamnophis s. proximus)* were also very common in the area. They were also found to be non-detrimental to ducks.

Some of the larger snakes that are known to eat game bird eggs were absent from or rare in the prairie nesting area. The black-snake *(Coluber constrictor constrictor)*, blue racer *(Coluber c. flaviventris)*, fox-snake *(Elaphe vulpina)*, pilot black-snake *(Elaphe obsoleta obsoleta)*, bull-snake *(Pituophis sayi)* and water-snake *(Natrix sipedon)* were all common in eastern and southern Iowa, but they were not recorded in the duck nesting area.

Snapping turtle (Chelydra serpentina). This turtle has for numerous reasons inherited a very unworthy reputation throughout the country. Strange as it may seem, only four individuals were actually observed during the course of the teal study in the prairie area of Iowa. Three were seen in Lost Island Lake, Clay County, Iowa, a deep water lake that was not frequented by ducklings; and the other turtle was captured on an old road near a marsh inhabited by many ducklings. There were certainly more snapping turtles present than were observed but because of their low population the duck mortality brought about by them, if any at all, was negligible.

Bell's painted turtle (Chrysemys picta bellii). Scores of these turtles were observed daily during the nesting and rearing season. During the duck nesting season female turtles were seen many times depositing eggs in sandy bluegrass knolls just a few feet from an incubating Blue-winged Teal. Often the turtles were observed on muskrat houses sunning themselves side by side with young and adult teal. But it was not found that this turtle interfered in any way with the well being of the Blue-winged Teal.

Blanding's turtle (Emys blandingii). About 15 Blanding's turtles were recorded in the study area over a span of five years. Their habits are similar to those of the Bell's painted turtles; and, like that turtle, they were not found to be a liability to the teal.

BIRDS

Marsh Hawk. The Marsh Hawk was a common nesting bird in northwestern Iowa throughout the course of the duck studies. Approximately one pair of Marsh Hawks nested per section of land in the waterfowl area each year. Contemporaneous with the duck studies, the food habits of the Marsh Hawk were worked out, principally by Dr. Paul L. Errington.

One hundred and sixty-nine gullet collections were taken from four nests of young in 1933, 109 gullet collections were taken from four nests of young in 1934, and 68 gullet collections were taken from four nests of young in 1935 (Errington and Breckenridge, 1936, p. 838). Of 557 items of food taken over the three-year period by the hawks, only once was that of a duck taken and that was a duckling, probably a Blue-winged Teal, taken the first week in July, 1933. The abundance of more accessible prey and the inability of the hawk to catch ducks was probably the reason for the nonmolestation of them. Table V (taken from Errington and Breckenridge, 1936) summarizes the food habits of the Marsh Hawks in the Ruthven, Iowa, area.

Throughout the duck rearing season Marsh Hawks were seen hunting and coursing over the rearing grounds. Many hours were spent observing the ducks in relation to the hunting habits of the hawks. Usually the mother teal guided her young into nearby cover at the approach of a Marsh Hawk. Often the intruder made a low sweep as if to retrieve a duckling, but not once did the author witness a kill.

After the duck mating season, Marsh Hawks were observed

TABLE V. *Proportions of summer prey taken by Marsh Hawks at Ruthven, Iowa*

Prey individuals	Number and percent of total			
	June to Aug., 1933	June to Sept., 1934	Mainly for July, 1935	Three seasons 1933 to 1935
Young Leporidae, mostly cottontails with a few jackrabbits	12 of 289 or 4.15 pct.	7 of 158 or 4.43 pct.	21 of 110 or 19.09 pct.	40 of 557 or 7.18 pct.
Mice, mostly meadow mice	3 or 1.04 pct.	9 or 5.7 pct.	3 or 2.73 pct.	15 or 2.67 pct.
Sciuridae, mostly ground squirrels	134 or 46.37 pct.	41 or 25.95 pct.	35 or 31.82 pct.	210 or 37.7 pct.
Undetermined mammal or probable mammal		2 or 1.27 pct.	1 or 0.9 pct.	3 or 0.54 pct.
Fringillidae	6 or 2.08 pct.	16 or 10.13 pct.	14 or 12.73 pct.	36 or 6.46 pct.
Grackles and blackbirds	41 or 14.19 pct.	11 or 6.96 pct.	2 or 1.82 pct.	54 or 9.7 pct.
Meadowlarks and a few other Icteridae	10 or 3.46 pct.	17 or 10.76 pct.	10 or 9.09 pct.	37 or 6.64 pct.
Miscellaneous passerine birds	8 or 2.77 pct.	2 or 1.27 pct.	6 or 5.45 pct.	16 or 2.87 pct.
Picidae, mostly flickers	17 or 5.88 pct.	6 or 3.79 pct.	2 or 1.82 pct.	25 or 4.49 pct.
Mourning doves	4 or 1.38 pct.	7 or 4.43 pct.		11 or 1.96 pct.
Rallidae, mostly Virginia rails and sora	4 or 1.38 pct.	8 or 5.06 pct.	1 or 0.9 pct.	13 or 2.33 pct.
Miscellaneous marsh birds, mostly terns	3 or 1.04 pct.	1 or 0.63 pct.	4 or 3.64 pct.	8 or 1.44 pct.
Young domestic chickens	7 or 2.42 pct.	6 or 3.79 pct.		13 or 2.33 pct.
Young ring-necked pheasants	12 or 4.15 pct	8 or 5.06 pct.	4 or 3.64 pct.	24 or 4.31 pct
Hungarian partridges, mostly young	5 or 1.73 pct.	2 or 1.27 pct.	2 or 1.82 pct.	9 or 1.62 pct.
Miscellaneous and undetermined birds, mostly probable passerines	15 or 5.19 pct.	11 or 6.96 pct.	1 or 0.09 pct.	27 or 4.85 pct.
Frogs	8 or 2.77 pct.	4 or 2.53 pct.	4 or 3.64 pct.	16 or 2.87 pct.

innumerable times flying over flocks of male teal, that paid little if any attention at all to the raptors. Entire flocks of ducks were observed sleeping, preening or feeding for an hour at a time while a Marsh Hawk repeatedly swerved over them. Several times during the fall and spring migrations flocks were seen to rise suddenly into the air at the approach of a Marsh Hawk, but no casualties were noted.

By correlating the food habits of the Marsh Hawk with the reactions of the ducks to the hawks it seemed as though the depredation upon the Blue-winged Teal by this bird was negligible.

Intervention of the Ring-necked Pheasant (Phasianus colchicus torquatus). The marsh regions in Iowa as a whole are the choice Ring-necked Pheasant production areas in the state. It was found that the pheasant parasitized a small percentage of the Blue-winged Teal nests during 1932 and 1935, as well as the nests of other marsh nesting birds (Bennett, 1936). Of 340 Puddle Duck nests observed in Iowa, 16 (4.7 percent) contained pheasant eggs (Table VI).

The largest clutch found was that of a Blue-winged Teal containing 14 teal eggs and 11 pheasant eggs. In only one case did the pheasant eggs outnumber the duck eggs. A number of

TABLE VI. *Parasitized nests*

Number and bird	No. eggs of nest building species	Pheasant eggs	Eggs of nest building species hatched	Pheasant eggs hatched
1 Mallard	6	3	6	0
2 "	7	3	7	0
3 "	7	3	7	0
1 Blue-winged Teal	11	1	11	0
2 " "	11	4	0	0
3 " "	6	3	6	1
4 " "	4	3	0	0
5 " "	9	1	0	0
6 " "	4	6	0	0
7 " "	14	11	0	0
8 " "	4	3	0	0
9 " "	8	1	8	1
10 " "	5	5	0	0
11 " "	3	3	3	0
12 " "	7	1	7	0
1 Shoveller	6	3	6	0

single pheasant eggs were found from several inches to several feet from duck nests. As Blue-winged Teal outnumbered all other nesting puddle ducks combined, more pheasant eggs were deposited in teal nests than in the nests of other ducks. Whether the duck nests were used as dumping nests merely through carelessness, or with nesting intentions by the pheasant, it would be difficult to ascertain. In all cases the nests were occupied by ducks and not by pheasants. In two instances the pheasant eggs hatched at the same time as those of the duck. One can imagine the situation that must have arisen when the duck took her brood to the marsh. With the exception of the teal nest containing 14 teal eggs and 11 pheasant eggs, all of the duck clutches contained less than the average number of duck eggs found in nests not parasitized by pheasants. It appeared that laying on the part of the duck ceased when the nest became filled; and, after incubation began, the depositing of pheasant eggs in the duck nest ceased. For a total of 277 normal Blue-winged Teal nests, the average clutch contained 9.44 eggs; for 84 Mallard nests the average was 10.6 eggs per clutch; for 13 Shoveller nests the average was 9 eggs per nest. On this basis the teal nests containing pheasant eggs averaged 7.16 duck eggs per clutch; the Mallard nests averaged 6.66 duck eggs; and the Shoveller nest contained six duck eggs. From these data, although few, it appears that pheasant eggs deposited in a duck nest reduce the potential number of duck eggs. The observations thus far have not revealed any physical strife between nesting pheasants and nesting ducks. Within a few feet of many duck nests pheasant nests have very frequently been observed. If there were any territorial difficulties existing between nesting ducks and pheasants, the effects were not in evidence.

Pheasant eggs were found in duck nests during the years 1933, 1934 and 1935. Throughout those years the pheasant population in the vicinity of Ruthven, Iowa, was about one bird to four or five acres. The severe winter of 1935-36 lowered the pheasant population in that area to approximately 1 bird to 20 acres. No parasitized duck nests were found the following duck nesting season. Perhaps the habit of depositing eggs in duck nests was because of an overcrowded pheasant nesting population. Future studies may prove that high pheasant populations are not desirable in a puddle duck nesting territory.

Great Horned Owl (Bubo virginianus virginianus). From 1933 to 1935, 151 Great Horned Owl pellets were gathered during Blue-winged Teal migration or residence in the Ruthven, Iowa, area (Errington and Frances Flint Hamerstrom, unpublished). Of these, 3 of 18 pellets collected July, 1933, contained remains of teal; 1 of the 3 pellets contained remains of both an adult and a large young. Only one other representation of Blue-winged Teal was found in the total pellet collection—a pellet from April or May, 1935. There was evidence of considerable pressure on other species of ducks, particularly during migration (may have been shot, crippled birds). Altogether, duck remains were contained in 30 of the total number of 280 pellets collected.

Because of the lack of suitable environment (timbered tracts) in the prairie area, the horned owl population was very low.

Eastern Crow (Corvus brachyrhynchos brachyrhynchos). A total of 12 nests, 4.8 percent, were destroyed by crows. The crow population in the duck nesting area was comparatively low. The breeding population was probably as low as one pair per section of land. In the prairie area the scarcity of trees means a lack of nesting habitat for crows. Many of the crows that remain to nest in northwestern Iowa have to sneak up to some farmer's woodlot to carry out their reproductive activities.

Crows probably eat duck eggs at every opportunity. Pecks of crow-destroyed eggs could have been gathered around the marshes each year at the beginning of the laying season. However, practically all such destroyed eggs had been promiscuously dropped over the countryside before the nesting season began. The destruction of those eggs did not represent destroyed nests.

It was found from limited observations (Errington and Bennett in South Dakota, unpublished) that crow depredations upon ducklings may be largely caused by exposure. Many instances of crows taking young ducks have been reported from the severe drought regions. Small ducklings forced into shrinking lakes and potholes with yards of sticky mud between them and the nearest cover would surely be at the mercy of many enemies such as crows, hawks or other flesh eaters; or they might mire down or die of thirst and hunger. Depredations might depend upon the number of ducklings rather than one of few crows or many crows.

NATIVE MAMMALS

Striped ground squirrel (Citellus tridecemlineatus). The striped ground squirrel is one of the most common mammals in the prairie area of Iowa. In some of the nesting areas 25 of these little rodents were recorded per acre. Even in such areas of concentration no nest destruction by them was noted.

Franklin's ground squirrel (Citellus franklini). This rodent was common in the region. However, the population was much lower than that of the striped ground squirrel. One and six-tenths percent of the teal nests was pilfered by this animal. It is possible that increased populations of the Franklin's ground squirrel could be an important factor in nest destruction.

Coyote (Canis latrans). Each year during the course of the duck studies there were two to six coyotes resident in the study area. No evidence was obtained that indicated the animal was a nest robber or a killer of ducklings. On May 19, 1933, a teal nest was found 50 yards from a den used by a female coyote and five pups. The author kept the nest under close observation to see what would happen. In spite of the close proximity of the nest to the den all of the ducklings hatched and made their way to the nearby marsh.

Fecal droppings were examined around two active dens but remnants of duck eggs were not present. The wings of a Mallard drake were found near one den. The refuse and droppings indicated that the animals had been living to a great extent upon ground squirrels, mice, shrews, cottontails, jack rabbits and miscellaneous birds.

Red fox (Vulpes regalis). The red fox was rarely encountered in the duck breeding area. A den of one female and six pups was found near a duck-producing marsh in 1934. The only duck remains found in fecal droppings or refuse around the den were those of one female Mallard and two Pintail drakes. No eggs or ducklings were found.

Gray fox (Urocyon cinereoargenteus). This fox was very rare or absent from the prairie region of Iowa.

Raccoon (Procyon lotor). The nonexistence of suitable timbered tracts in the prairie section kept this animal from being present around many of the duck nesting areas. Specimens, fecal droppings and other signs were absent; thus it was impossible and unnecessary to consider this fur bearer as a predator of Blue-winged Teal in the Ruthven area.

Long-tailed weasel (Mustela longicauda). No direct evidence was obtained as to the destructiveness of this little carnivore. It was present in limited numbers. Errington (1936, pp. 406-407) reported upon the food habits of a weasel family (prob-

FIG. 22. Teal nest three feet from striped skunk den. Eight eggs had been deposited before the nest was destroyed.

ably this species) in the study area. He found that small mammals, insects and song birds were present in 32 fecal samples.

Mink (Mustela vison). This mammal, the second most valuable fur bearer in Iowa, was common on all of the marshes. Two female teal on the nest (0.8 percent of the nests) were killed by mink. In both instances the eggs were not disturbed by the raiding animal.

Mink took comparatively few ducklings. The remains of three ducklings were detected in fecal droppings from several hundred samples. About 30 dens and 12 caches were examined in the study area. No remains of ducklings were found in the dens. The remains of three ducklings were found in 12 caches. From June 15 to July 15 each year practically every fecal dropping showed remains of American Coot chicks. The abundance, unwariness and availability of the coot chicks may have acted as a buffer agency for the Blue-winged Teal ducklings.

Striped skunk (Mephitis mesomelas). Among the fur bearers, the striped skunk was surpassed in numbers only by the muskrat. Every duck nesting margin had resident skunks. Six nests, 2.4 percent, were destroyed by this animal. Heavy yearly trapping usually kept the skunk and mink populations down to a fairly low level. However, for some reason the skunk population began an abnormal increase in 1934. By the breeding season of 1936 the population had risen greatly in spite of trapping. The recorded nest destruction occurred in 1935 and 1936 along with a definite increase in the skunk population. If large numbers of skunks in a duck nesting area developed an egg-eating habit, a great amount of nest destruction could easily occur.

Figure 22 shows a teal nest that was situated just three feet from an active skunk den. The eggs were not eaten until a complement of eight eggs had been deposited in the nest. This destroyed nest might have been attributed to the lack of wariness on the part of the teal, instead of depredations caused by skunks.

Spotted skunk (Spilogale interrupta). The spotted skunk was not nearly so common as the striped skunk. No observations were made that labeled this animal as an eater of teal eggs. Some of the nest destruction under the column "unknown mammal" may have been caused by it.

American badger (Taxidea taxus). It was thought by some people about five years ago that this prairie animal was doomed for extinction in the state. Surprisingly, the big carnivore has become more or less common over most of the prairie section of Iowa since that time. The animal did not receive any more legislative protection than in the preceding years. His pelt value has gone up in price, thus encouraging heavier trapping. However, by 1936 each nest area was supporting a fair badger population. The eggs of three nests, 1.1 percent of the total number of nests, under observation were destroyed by the badger in 1936.

Errington, during the summer of 1936, analyzed 37 badger droppings collected in the Ruthven area. Five of the 37 fecal droppings contained remains of Blue-winged Teal eggs. Errington (1937) stated the following concerning some nest observations made in 1936: "Nests of ground nesting birds seem to be rifled as the badgers may chance to run across them. On an estimated total of 2.3 acres carefully worked over in the neighborhood of the badger diggings and apparent hunting grounds, three Blue-winged Teal and two pheasant nests were found. The two pheasant nests and two of the teal nests hatched successfully, while the third nest—situated 35 feet from the nearest of a set of well-used badger holes—was destroyed. An incomplete clutch of four teal eggs was accidentally discovered on May 12; the female flushed violently and did not return, and the eggs were eaten after the manner of badgers some weeks after desertion."

INFERTILE EGGS

One nest of nine eggs, 0.4 percent of the nests, was unsuccessful because of infertile eggs. Nine single infertile eggs were found, 0.7 percent of eggs in successful nests, in 9 of the 133 successful nests .

EFFECT OF NEST STUDIES

It was found at the beginning of the nest studies that freshly made paths, trampled grass and weeds, film wrappings, nest markers and other disturbances in the immediate vicinity of a nest were very likely to attract predators. Thus, in making trips to a nest the author never approached from the same direction more than once. If there was any trampling of grasses near the nest, the grasses were always brushed back into a normal position before leaving. The nest marker, a strip of muslin one inch wide and eight inches long, was tied to a grass or weed at least 15 yards from the nest in order that curious animals would not be led to the nest. When looking for nests or revisiting nests a close watch was kept for lurking crows. If they appeared, all work ceased until they had passed on to the next section of land. This precaution was taken to prevent the crows from seeing a duck flush from a nest and locating the nest site.

Two nests, 0.8 percent, were known to have been abandoned because of poor study technique during the inaugural stages of the work.

PARASITES AND DISEASES

Parasites and diseases played an unimportant part in the juvenile mortality in the Ruthven marshes during the course of the study. No diseased ducklings, dead or alive, were observed.

Sooter (1937, p. 108) during the summer of 1936 found leeches *(Theromyzon occidentalis)* infesting the young of the American Coot, Pied-billed Grebe and Blue-winged Teal in the Ruthven area. It was found that the leeches invaded the nasal cavity of the young birds. Four of six teal ducklings taken from July 27 to August 21 were parasitized by leeches. Although some of the coot chicks succumbed to the leech infestations, no teal were found dying from this cause. Further studies of the leech as a parasite of the Blue-winged Teal may reveal a serious potential cause of high mortality.

PERCENTAGE OF YOUNG REACHING THE MIGRATORY STAGE

Throughout the rearing seasons of 1933, 1934, 1935 and 1936 weekly counts of young ducks and adult females were made. Those counts could not be called brood counts because the number of individuals per brood may vary from day to day. The willingness of ducklings to abandon their mother for some other brooding female caused the author to discard the term, "Brood Count." However, young ducks and adult females were recorded as to age (ducklings and adult females) and not broods. It was concluded that the weekly totals indicated the average juvenile losses from week to week. The recordings of the four years are shown in Tables VII, VIII, IX and X.

TABLE VII. *Counts of adults with young, 1933*

Period	Ducklings seen	Adult females	Average no. young per female
June 24–July 16	195	30	6.5

Errington and Bennett (1934, p. 250) carried on the observations tabulated in Table VII. The 6.5 juveniles represent the number reared at the end of the first half of the rearing season. The rate of recession of young to the middle of July corresponds closely to the data obtained in 1934 (Table VIII) and 1936 (Table X). At the same rate of recession as in 1934 and 1936 the number of juveniles at the beginning of the migratory season would be about five young to one adult female.

TABLE VIII. *Counts of adults with young, 1934*

Period	Ducklings seen	Adult females	Average no. young per female
July 1–7	32	4	8
July 8–13	46	6	7.7
July 14–20	114	15	7.6
July 21–27	26	4	6.5
July 28–Aug. 3	131	25	5.2
Aug. 4–10	126	25	5
Aug. 11–17	156	30	5.2

TABLE IX. *Counts of adults with young, 1935*

Period	Ducklings seen	Adult females	Average no. young per female
July 7–Aug. 19	310	53	5.87

The data in Table IX were obtained by Mr. B. V. Travis, Department of Zoology and Entomology, Iowa State College. If the figures had been listed weekly, in all probability the counts made during the last week of the observations would show a lower weekly average for that week than the average for the entire period. By using the same rate of recession as found in 1934 and 1936 the average for the last week of observations would be about five ducklings per adult female.

TABLE X. *Counts of adults with young, 1936*

Period	Ducklings seen	Adult females	Average no. young per female
July 1-7	23	3	7.7
July 8-13	76	8	7.6
July 14-20	79	11	7.2
July 21-27	162	31	5.2
July 28-Aug. 3	146	28	5.2
Aug. 4-10	138	27	5.1
Aug. 11-17	107	17	5.1

As the average normal nest contained 9.3 eggs and 0.7 percent of which were infertile, 9.24 eggs produced young from each normal nest that was successful. Thus, for every 9.24 young plus 0.01 duckling for successful renesting eggs, 5.1 young (55 percent) reached the migratory stage the later days of August.

NUMBER OF YOUNG REACHING THE MIGRATORY STAGE PER NESTING PAIR OF ADULTS

The number of ducklings reared to the migratory stage per nesting pair of teal, 1932-36, may be estimated by correlating the nest losses with the juvenile losses over the same period. Fifty-nine and six-tenths percent of the normal nests was successful over the five-year period. Thus, of 100 nests, 59.6 produced young. Nine and twenty-five hundredths eggs per successful nest gave a total of 551 eggs. Adding 10 ducklings from successful renesting results in a total of 561 ducklings, 55 percent, or 309 ducklings, reached the migratory stage per 100 nests in Iowa, 1932-36. Or, each pair of Blue-winged Teal under the writer's observation that stopped to nest in Iowa from 1932 to 1936 started south each fall with 3.09 young ducks.

CHAPTER X

Nesting Cover

Before the days of settlement in Iowa the uplands that surrounded the prairie water areas supported rank growths of native grasses and other native prairie plants. Today those plants have been eliminated by cultivation and grazing. Because the margins around most of the existing water areas were too wet to cultivate, they were utilized for grazing. Grazing eliminated the native grasses and in their place were found bluegrass, weeds and a few remnants of native prairie plants. In some of the low margins slough grass was found, which was mowed each year for feeding and packing purposes. However, as in some years the mowing operations were not carried out until late in July, the breeding ducks that hid their nests in it were not disturbed.

Many of the higher well-drained margins were cultivated and sown to corn *(Zea mays)*, wheat *(Triticum aestivum)* or oats *(Avena sativa)*. Such plantings practically eliminated successful nesting attempts. In other years the same areas were planted to alfalfa *(Medicago sativa)*. Alfalfa seemed to be very attractive to nesting teal. Ordinarily alfalfa was mowed the first week in June, a practice which resulted in the complete destruction of nests found therein.

Following are listed the main types of nesting cover found in Iowa and their relative importance.

Bluegrass. Bluegrass, the most common type of nesting cover found in Iowa, constituted the cover of 160 nests (47 percent). At the time of nest building the grass was 8 to 10 inches in height (fig. 23). By the time the hatching date arrived the

Fig. 23. A bluegrass nesting area. (Photo by H. H. Knight.)

grass was 12 to 16 inches high. Other plants such as lesser ragweed *(Ambrosia artemisiifolia)*, beard grass *(Andropogon scoparius)*, hoary vervain *(Verbena urticaefolia)*, milkweeds (*Asclepias* spp.), squirrel-tail grass *(Hordeum jubatum)* and spike rushes (*Eleocharis* spp.) were found as supporting cover with the bluegrass. About 30 percent of the nests was found in bluegrass interspersed with a few of the above plants. Pure stands of bluegrass seemed to be preferred to mixed growths of bluegrass and forbs.

Slough Grass (Spartina michauxiana). One hundred and thirty-two nests, 38.8 percent, were found in slough grass. The grass was from 18 to 24 inches in height at the beginning of the nesting season. By the end of June, at the time when most of the ducklings hatch, it was between 30 and 40 inches in height. The heaviest nesting concentration was found in that type of nesting cover (fig. 24). Twenty-one duck nests (12 teal and 9 mallard) were found in the summer of 1932 on a 22-acre tract covered with slough grass.

In some of the slough grass areas there were found many other plants that helped to make up the nesting cover. About

Fig. 24. Slough grass nesting cover. (Photo by H. H. Knight).

7 percent of the nests found in slough grass also had some of the following plants immediately around the nest as supporting cover: Squirrel-tail grass, hedge nettle *(Stachys tenuifolia)*, reed *(Phragmites communis)*, bluegrass, spike rushes, sedges (*Cyperus* spp.), sedges (*Carex* spp.), river bulrush *(Scirpus fluviatilus)*, wild rye *(Elymus canadensis)*, lesser ragweed, goldenrods (*Solidago* spp.), milkweed, larger blue flag *(Iris versicolor)* and sweet flag *(Acorus Calamus)*.

Alfalfa cover. The alfalfa acreage near the marshy areas was very small. However, practically every marsh had one or more small fields (5 to 10 acres) of alfalfa within nesting distance of the water area. Nests were found each year in every field. In years of normal rainfall alfalfa was mowed during the first week in June, resulting in the destruction of the nests. However, in the spring of 1935, due to prolonged wet weather, it was impossible to cut the alfalfa until the first week in July. This delay allowed 95 percent of the ducklings to hatch safely. Over a four-year period 48 nests (14 percent) were found in alfalfa fields, averaging a nest per acre each year.

At the beginning of the nesting season the alfalfa was 8 to 10 inches in height. By the end of the first week in June (mowing time) it was usually 14 to 16 inches high.

It may be that the Blue-winged Teal preferred alfalfa to native prairie vegetation for nesting cover. One alfalfa field adjoined a similar tract of native prairie. Over a four-year period the alfalfa supported one nest per acre while the native prairie vegetation area attracted no nesting ducks. On the other hand alfalfa fields situated near bluegrass areas carried about the same number of nests as did the bluegrass tracts. Although the comparative data are few, there is an indication that alfalfa and bluegrass may be more desirable teal nesting cover than native prairie vegetation.

CHAPTER XI

Rearing Cover

Between 5,000 and 6,000 ducklings were observed in northwest Iowa in 1932-36. The presence of ducklings in the respective types of cover combinations indicated to a high degree of reliability the value of such plant associations as rearing cover. The author classed the rearing cover plant combinations into six main types. Each of the six types is discussed in the order of importance.

1. Great bulrush *(Scirpus validus)*, round bulrush *(Scirpus occidentalis)* and river bulrush *(Scirpus fluviatilis)* associes.

About 30 percent of the ducklings was observed inhabiting this type of rearing cover (fig. 25). The plants in this combination usually grew in water one to two feet deep. Many of the Iowa marshes had a band of this cover combination 50 to 150 feet between the shore and deeper waters. As the water became deeper toward the middle of the marsh the round bulrush became the dominant plant, the great and river bulrush not being adapted to such deep water.

This type of cover combination is very attractive to muskrats. The houses built by the muskrats become available as roosting and waiting sites within a year or so.

2. River bulrush *(Scirpus fluviatilis)*, great bulrush *(Scirpus validus)* and bur-reed *(Sparganium eurycarpum)*, associes.

These plants were usually observed in this combination, in

FIG. 25. Rearing cover of bulrushes *(Scirpus validus, S. occidentalis,* and *S. fluviatilis)*.

FIG. 26. *(left)* Rearing cover of river bulrush and cat-tail. FIG. 27. *(right)* Rearing cover of bur-reed, sweet flag and larger blue flag.

water 12 to 18 inches deep. Approximately 25 percent of the juveniles was observed in this combination of cover. Perhaps the density of this group of plants was too great to be as attractive to the young teal and mother as the preceding combination.

3. River bulrush *(Scirpus fluviatilis)* and cat-tail *(Typha latifolia)*, associes.

The main value of these plants is their ability to persist in shallow areas that lose most of the water late in the summer. Rains and thaws the following spring refill the water basins and this combination thrives, providing rearing cover by July 1. Twenty percent of the young was reared in this group of plants (fig. 26).

4. River bulrush *(Scirpus fluviatilis)* and sedge *(Carex riparia)*, associes.

About 10 percent of the young teal was seen most of the time in this growth of vegetation. These two species of plants in combination are found in water six inches to three feet deep. This combination was more common in a newly flooded or restored marsh. If the water depth was maintained at two or three feet over a two- to three-year period the combination of plants in type plants, No. 1, become the dominants, the sedge *(Carex riparia)* not being adapted to sustained propagation in deep water. Apparently these plants grew in such profusion that the vegetation matted and tangled to such a degree that they made swimming difficult for the ducks.

5. Reed *(Phragmites communis)* and cat-tail *(Typha latifolia)*, associes.

Only 5 percent of the young was observed in this habitat.

Apparently the tall, rank growths of these plants crowded out food plants and shut off the sunshine. Growths of this combination were found growing in water 6 to 24 inches deep.

6. Bur-reed *(Sparganium eurycarpum)*, sweet flag *(Acorus Calamus)* and larger blue flag *(Iris versicolor)*, associes.

Five percent of the juveniles was reared in growths of these plants. These plants in combination were usually found growing profusely in water 6 to 16 inches deep. The growth appeared to be too dense to be attractive for many broods (fig. 27).

Miscellaneous cover. About 5 percent of the observed young was reared in a variety of plant formations. One brood of young was known to have been reared in a pure stand of prairie smartweed *(Polygonum Muhlenbergii)*. A few broods were observed in slough grass. Young willows (*Salix* sp.) were observed in one case sheltering a brood of young teal. One pond, grown mostly to arrowhead *(Sagittaria latifolia)*, served as a rearing area for a brood of young. Spike rush (*Eleocharis* sp.) was used as rearing cover in one instance.

CHAPTER XII

Food Habits

The food habits of many of the native ducks in the United States have been studied. One of the most comprehensive food habits researches was that carried out by Douglas C. Mabbott, U. S. Bureau of Biological Survey (1920). His publication, *Food Habits of Seven Species of American Shoal-Water Ducks,* contained data concerning the food found in 319 Blue-winged Teal stomachs, collected in 29 states and 4 Canadian Provinces over a 31-year period, and in every month except January (Tables XI and XII).

The author analyzed the contents of 19 Blue-winged Teal stomachs collected during October and November, 1933, in the vicinity of Ruthven, Iowa (Table XIV). The stomachs of 26 juveniles (three days to six weeks old) were collected during the summers of 1933-36 in the vicinity of Ruthven, Iowa (Table XIII). The stomachs of 21 Blue-winged Teal were collected in Mexico during December, 1936, and January, 1937 (Table XV).

TABLE XI. *Items of vegetable food identified in the stomachs of 319 Blue-winged Teal and the number of stomachs in which found. (Mabbott's findings, 1920)*

Kind of food	No. of stomachs in which found
Total number of stomachs examined	319
Subkingdom EUTHALLOPHYTA	
Unidentified algae	4
Chara sp. (musk grass)	31
Subkingdom SPERMATOPHYTA	
Sparganiaceae	
Sparganium androcladum (bur-reed)	2
Sparganium sp. (bur-reed)	39
Naiadaceae	
Potamogeton natans (floating pondweed)	1

TABLE XI—*Continued*

Kind of food	No. of stomachs in which found
Potamogeton sp. (unidentified pondweeds)	150
Ruppia maritima (widgeon grass)	87
Zannichellia palustris (horned pondweed)	2
Zostera marina (eelgrass)	3
Najas marina (large bushy pondweed)	1
Najas flexilis (bushy pondweed)	17
Alismaceae	
Sagittaria latifolia (wapato)	1
Sagittaria sp. (unidentified arrowheads)	4
Alisma plantago-aquatica (water plantain)	1
Alisma sp. (water plantain)	1
Hydrocharitaceae	
Philotria sp. (waterweed)	2
Vallisneria spiralis (wild celery)	1
Vallisneria sp. (wild celery)	1
Gramineae	
Unidentified grasses	24
Panicum sp. (switch grass)	18
Echinochloa crus-galli (wild millet)	1
Echniochloa sp. (cockspur grass)	1
Chaetochloa glauca (foxtail)	5
Chaetochloa viridis (green foxtail)	1
Chaetochloa sp. (foxtail)	8
Zizania palustris (wild rice)	22
Zizaniopsis miliacea (cut-grass)	1
Homalocenchrus oryzoides (rice cut-grass)	9
Oryza sativa (cultivated rice)	12
Spartina sp. (salt-marsh grass)	1
Sporobolus sp. (rush-grass)	1
Monanthochloe littoralis	13
Puccinellia nutalliana	3
Zea mays (cultivated corn)	1
Cyperaceae	
Unidentified sedges	27
Cyperus sp. (chufa)	45
Dulichium arundinaceum (three-ways sedge)	1
Eleocharis sp. (spike rush)	33
Fimbristylis sp.	40
Scirpus americanus (three-square)	10
Scirpus paludosus (prairie bulrush)	7
Scirpus robustus (salt-marsh bulrush)	2
Scirpus fluviatilis (river bulrush)	18
Scirpus validus (great bulrush)	2
Scirpus sp. (unidentified bulrushes)	184
Rhynchospora sp. (beaked rush)	2
Cladium effusum (saw grass)	46
Cladium mariscoides (twig-rush)	9
Carex decomposita (panicled sedge)	2
Carex sp. (sedge)	57
Lemnaceae	
Lemna sp. (unidentified duckweeds)	14
Pontederiaceae	
Heteranthera dubia (water star-grass)	1

TABLE XI—*Continued*

Kind of food	No. of stomachs in which found
Salicaceae	
Salix sp. (willow, galls)	1
Myricaceae	
Myrica sp. (unidentified myrtles)	18
Polygonaceae	
Rumex sp. (dock)	2
Polygonum amphibium (water smartweed)	27
Polygonum hydropiper (water pepper)	10
Polygonum hydropiperoides (mild water pepper)	31
Polygonum lapathifolium (dock-leaved smartweed)	26
Polygonum opelousanum (smartweed)	7
Polygonum pennsylvanicum (Pennsylvania smartweed)	3
Polygonum persicaria (lady's thumb)	10
Polygonum portolicense (dense-flowered smartweed)	1
Polygonum sagittatum (arrow-leaved smartweed)	11
Poylgonum sp. (unidentified smartweeds)	16
Chenopodiaceae	
Chenopodium sp. (pigweed)	1
Amaranthaceae	
Amaranthus sp. (pigweed)	5
Caryophyllaceae	
Unidentified	1
Ceratophyllaceae	
Ceratophyllum demersum (coontail, hornwort)	7
Nymphaeaceae	
Castalia sp. (waterlily)	14
Brasenia schreberi (water shield)	13
Ranunculaceae	
Ranunculus delphinifolius (yellow water-crowfoot)	1
Ranunculus sp. (crowfoot)	6
Hamamelidaceae	
Liquidambar styraciflua (sweet gum)	7
Rosaceae	
Crataegus sp. (hawthorn)	1
Fragaria sp. (strawberry)	1
Rubus sp. (bramble)	15
Leguminosae	
Trifolium sp. (clover)	3
Melilotus sp. (sweet clover)	3
Euphorbiaceae	
Croton texensis	1
Anacardiaceae	
Rhus sp. (unidentified sumacs)	2
Aquifoliaceae	
Ilex sp. (holly)	5
Vitaceae	
Vitis sp. (grapes)	2
Malvaceae	
Sida spinosa (nail grass)	2
Malva sp. (mallow)	1
Hibiscus sp. (rose mallow)	2

TABLE XI—*Continued*

Kind of food	No. of stomachs in which found
Lythraceae	
Decodon verticillatus (swamp loosestrife, willow herb)	1
Onagraceae	
Jussiaea sp. (primrose willow)	6
Haloragidaceae	
Myriophyllum sp. (water milfoil)	44
Proserpinaca sp. (mermaid weed)	5
Hippuris vulgaris (bottle brush)	8
Umbelliferae	
Hydrocotyle sp. (water pennywort)	12
Centella asiatica (marsh pennywort)	2
Ericaceae	
Gaultheria sp. (wintergreen)	2
Convolvulaceae	
Cuscuta sp. (dodder)	11
Boraginaceae	
Heliotropium indicum (wild heliotrope)	16
Verbenaceae	
Verbena sp. (verbena)	11
Lippia sp. (fog-fruit)	13
Plantaginaceae	
Plantago sp. (plantain)	1
Rubiaceae	
Galium sp. (cleavers)	10
Diodia teres (rough buttonweed)	1
Cephalanthus occidentalis (buttonbush)	5
Caprifoliaceae	
Sambucus sp. (elder)	1
Compositae	
Ambrosia artemisifolia (ragweed)	3
Ambrosia sp. (ragweed)	5
Bidens sp. (bur marigold)	2
Taraxacum sp. (dandelion)	1

TABLE XII. *Items of animal food identified in the stomachs of 319 Blue-winged Teal and the number of stomachs in which found. (Mabbott's findings, 1920)*

Kind of food	No. of stomachs in which found
Total number of stomachs examined	319
Subkingdom ARTHROPODA	
Class Crustacea (Crustaceans)	
Unidentified	5
Order OSTRACODA	
Unidentified ostracods (bivalved crustaceans)	8
Order AMPHIPODA	
Unidentified	4
Gammaridae	
Gammarus locusta	1

TABLE XII—*Continued*

Kind of food	No. of stomachs in which found
Orchestiidae	
Hyalella knickerbockeri	1
Hyalella dentata	1
Order DECAPODA	
Suborder Macrura	
Crangonidae	
Crangonyx gracilis (shrimp)	1
Suborder Brachyura	
Unidentified crabs	1
Class Insecta (Insects)	
Unidentified insect fragments, eggs, larvae and pupae	14
Superorder AMPHIBIOTICA	
Unidentified damselflies or dragonflies and nymphs	3
Order ZYGOPTERA (Damselflies)	
Agrionidae	
Enallagma sp.	2
Order ANISOPTERA (Dragonflies)	
Unidentified dragonflies and nymphs	22
Order ORTHOPTERA (Grasshoppers, etc.)	
Unidentified grasshoppers and their eggs	1
Order HETEROPTERA (True bugs)	
Unidentified bugs	2
Corixidae (water boatmen)	
Corixa sp.	43
Belostomatidae (giant water bugs)	
Belostoma sp.	1
Naucoridae (creeping water bugs)	
Pelocoris femoratus	2
Pelocoris sp.	13
Notonectidae (back-swimmers)	
Notonecta sp.	1
Plea striola	11
Gerridae (water-striders)	
Gerris. sp.	2
Mesoveliidae	
Mesovelia mulsanti	2
Pentatomidae (stink bugs)	
Memecles incertus	1
Corimelaenidae	
Corimelaena nitiduloides	1
Order HOMOPTERA	
Fulgoridae	
Unidentified	1
Jassidae (leafhoppers)	1
Order NEUROPTERA	
Sialidae (dobson, etc.)	1
Order PHYRYGANOIDEO (Caddis flies)	
Unidentified larvae and cases	31

TABLE XII—*Continued*

Kind of food	No. of stomachs in which found
Order LEPIDOPTERA (Butterflies and Moths)	
Tineidae, cocoon	3
Order COLEOPTERA (Beetles)	
Unidentified fragments and larvae	50
Carabidae (ground beetles)	
Unidentified	3
Aspidoglossa subangulata	1
Bembidium intermedium	1
Platynus sp.	1
Chlaenius sp.	1
Selenophorus sp.	1
Anisodactylus dulcicollis	1
Anisodactylus rusticus	1
Haliplidae (crawling water beetles)	
Haliplus unicolor	1
Halipus sp.	2
Peltodytes simplex	1
Peltodytes sp.	4
Dytiscidae (predacious diving beetles)	
Unidentified adults and larvae	8
Colpius inflatus	3
Canthydrus bicolor	1
Hydrocanthus iricolor	1
Bidessus affinis	2
Bidessus flavicollis	1
Bidessus sp.	2
Coelambus turbidus	1
Hydroporus sp.	1
Coptotomus interrogatus	1
Agabus sp.	1
Gyrinidae (whirligig beetles)	
Gyrinus sp.	1
Hydrophilidae (water scavenger beetles)	
Unidentified beetles and larvae	11
Helophorus sp.	3
Berosus pantherinus	2
Berosus sp.	6
Philhydrus sp.	1
Histeridae	
Hister sp.	1
Byrrhidae	1
Heteroceridae	
Heterocerus sp.	2
Scarabaeidae (leaf chafers)	
Onthophagus hecate	1
Aphodius sp.	1
Phyllophaga sp. (May beetles)	1
Chrysomelidae (leaf beetles)	
Unidentified	2
Donacia sp.	2
Prasocuris phellandrii	1
Phyllotreta sp.	1

TABLE XII—*Continued*

Kind of food	No. of stomachs in which found
Suborder Rhynchophora (Weevils)	
Unidentified adults	8
Curculionidae (snout beetles)	
Unidentified	1
Lixellus filiformis	1
Sphenophorus aequalis	1
Sphenophorus sp.	3
Order DIPTERA (Flies)	
Unidentified adults, larvae and pupae	8
Chironomidae (midges)	
Unidentified adults, larvae and pupae	10
Ceratopogon sp.	1
Simuliidae	
Simulium sp.	1
Stratiomyidae (soldier flies)	
Unidentified larvae	11
Syrphidae (flower flies)	
Unidentified larvae and pupae	4
Anthomyiidae, adults	1
Ephydridae (brine flies), larvae and pupae	1
Order HYMENOPTERA (Ants, Bees and Wasps)	
Unidentified adults and cocoons	1
Ichneumonoidea (Parasitic wasps)	
Ichneumonidae	
Amblyteles sp.	1
Formicoidea (Ants)	
Formicidae	
Unidentified	18
Class Arachnida	
Order PSEUDOSCORPIONIDA	
Unidentified	1
Order ARANEIDA (Spiders)	
Unidentified	3
Order ACARIDA (Mites)	
Hydrachnidae (water mites)	22
Subkingdom MOLLUSCA (Mollusks)	
Unidentified	106
Class Pelecypoda (Bivalves)	
Unidentified	2
Cyrenidae	
Sphaerium sp.	3
Pisidium sp.	2
Class Gastropoda (Univalves)	
Amnicolidae	
Amnicola porata	2
Amnicola sp.	3

TABLE XII—*Continued*

Kind of food	No. of stomachs in which found
Physidae	
Physa heterostropha	2
Physa gyrina	1
Physa sp.	3
Lymnaeidae	
Lymnaea columella	2
Lymnaea desidiosa	1
Lymnaea palustris	1
Planorbis bicarinata	1
Planorbis duryi	1
Planorbis glabratum	2
Planorbis parvus	4
Planorbis trivolvis	4
Planorbis sp.	1
Valvatidae	
Valvata tricarinata	1
Subkingdom CHORDATA (Vertebrates)	
Class Pisces (Fishes)	
Unidentified, teeth, scales, etc.	3
Poeciliidae	
Fundulus sp.	2

TABLE XIII. *Items of food found in stomachs of 26 Blue-winged Teal ducklings and the number of stomachs in which found*
Iowa, July-August, 1933-36

Kind of food	No. of stomachs in which found
Vegetable	26
Chara sp.	8
Scirpus occidentalis	26
Scirpus validus	26
Scirpus fluviatilis	3
Potamogeton pectinatus	19
Potamogeton pusillus	2
Potamogeton sp.	6
Echinochloa crusgalli	2
Cyperus sp.	7
Carex riparia	22
Polygonum Muhlenbergii	2
Polygonum amphibium	7
Lemna sp.	14
Animal	12
Insects	9
Corixa sp.	9
Gerris sp.	4
Unidentified	4
Molluscs (unidentified)	5

TABLE XIV. *Items of food identified in the stomachs of 19 Blue-winged Teal collected in Iowa*

October-November, 1932

Kind of food	No. of stomachs in which found
Vegetable	19
Chara sp.	4
Scirpus occidentalis	19
Scirpus validus	16
Potamogeton gemmiparus	11
Potamogeton pusillus	4
Potamogeton sp.	8
Zea mays	2
Cyperus sp.	4
Polygonum lapathifolium	3
Polygonum persicaria	14
Animal	0

TABLE XV. *Items of food identified in the stomachs of 21 Blue-winged Teal collected in Mexico, December 25, 1936-January 7, 1937, by Mr. C. E. Gillham and Logan J. Bennett*

Kind of food	No of stomachs in which found
Vegetable	21
Chara sp.	3
Scirpus sp.	16
Potamogeton sp.	11
Polygonum sp.	1
Zea mays	1
Unidentified plant material	1
Animal	3
Insects (unidentified)	2
Crustaceans (unidentified)	3

Approximately 75 percent of the food eaten by the Blue-winged Teal consisted of plant material. There were 38 families of plants represented in the stomachs examined in Tables XI, XII, XIII, XIV and XV. The four families, Cyperaceae, Najadaceae, Gramineae and Polygonaceae, were by far the most common groups represented in the 385 stomachs (Table XVI). The high rate of occurrence of the species in these four families at least indicates what foods are preferred or the accessibility of such foods. It is interesting to note that the Cyperaceae, in addition to being the family represented most commonly in the stomachs, also constitute the most important group of plants making up the rearing cover on the breeding marsh.

TABLE XVI. *Summary of food contents of the 385 Blue-winged Teal stomachs*

Vegetable	
Families	Percentage of food in 385 stomachs
Cyperaceae	21.1
Najadaceae	14.3
Gramineae	14.1
Polygonaceae	8.20
Chara	2.86
Nymphaeceae	1.29
Haloragidaceae	.70
Sparganiaceae	.36
Rubiaceae	.31
Miscellaneous	11.80
Total	75.02
Animal	
Mollusca	14.11
Insecta	9.23
Crustacea	1.82
Miscellaneous	.31
Total	25.47

Animal food constituted about 25 percent of the food eaten by the Blue-winged Teal. Of the invertebrate animal foods eaten, insects and molluscs outnumbered by far the other forms. The insects belonging to the orders Hemiptera, Coleoptera and Anisoptera were the most frequently taken. The molluscs were represented mostly by a large number of unidentified species. The vertebrates were represented by fishes found in five stomachs.

The animal food, although probably of great importance in the diet of the Blue-winged Teal, was secondary to plant foods. The 26 duckling stomachs collected in Iowa indicated that animal food was an important item of diet during the rearing season, although the plant foods were of greater occurrence.

CHAPTER XIII

Nesting Populations

In evaluating the status of a species it is of utmost importance to know if possible the yearly fluctuations of populations in the respective types of breeding areas. There are three factors that may cause yearly variations in populations: (1) Increase or decrease of the entire population; (2) the habitability of the breeding area types from year to year; and (3) the geographical location of the breeding area types. Each factor is discussed below in the order named.

Increase or decrease of the entire population. The variation of the total population of waterfowl during any given year results from variation from the norm average among one or more of several changeable factors. Overshooting or undershooting, a poor nesting season or a favorable nesting season, a poor rearing season or a good rearing season may result in a low or high population the following year in some or all areas.

The desirabiltiy of the breeding area types from year to year. Drought, drainage, flooding, cultivation or grazing may vary the attractiveness of a breeding area type from year to year or permanently. The remaining marsh and nesting areas in Iowa are relatively safe from future drainage and cultivation. Drought, grazing and flooding, however, varied the breeding populations from year to year over the five-year period of research.

Geographical location of the breeding area types. The geographical location of an area seemed to play an important part in attracting breeding populations. It was known that the Blue-winged Teal population suffered greatly during 1932-35 over most of its breeding range. In spite of the decreasing population of the species the Ruthven area supported nesting teal during 1932 to 1936 in the habitable nesting portions. It appeared that migrating birds filled up the breeding environment each spring. As Iowa is on the southern edge of the true prairie breeding area type, thousands of teal utilized its waters during the spring flights. Thus, from all indications the desirable portions of the Ruthven area were inhabited by nesting teal regardless of the total population or the presence of other favorable breeding areas to the north, east or west.

The restoration of a million acres of teal breeding habitat in Iowa, Nebraska, South Dakota and North Dakota might hold breeding birds in those states that previously nested in Alberta, Canada.

As stated above, the teal nesting population 1932 to 1936 remained about the same in habitable environment in the Ruthven area. The desirability of portions of the area varied greatly over the period. In 1934 drought and overgrazing combined eliminated about 75 percent of the nesting cover for nesting purposes. The 25 percent of suitable environment carried no more nesting birds than the two previous years. In 1935 with nearly normal rainfall the area again supported as many nesting teal as in 1932-33. During that year it was known that the total teal population was less than during the previous years. In 1936, with an increase of teal (entire population) because of restricted shooting in 1935 and better breeding conditions in 1936, there was not an increase of nesting ducks in the Ruthven area. The area apparently carried its capacity of nesting birds each year according to its habitability.

Nesting was not uniform in distribution in the Ruthven area during any one year. But the distribution for each year was about the same in nestable margins. The heaviest concentration of nesting ducks found was one nest per acre on an area as large as 21 acres. On a 22-acre tract in 1932, with cover chiefly of slough grass, 12 teal and 9 Mallard nests were found. Similar nesting densities were found on some tracts during 1933-36. On several occasions in each year on small ungrazed and properly grazed arms of one-quarter acre in area, extending into a marsh, as many as three to five nests were found. In Iowa the average marsh with some nesting cover had a nesting population of 1 nest per 10 to 20 acres of margin. As a rule, at present, one nest per five acres is exceptionally high for the entire margin of Iowa marshes.

CHAPTER XIV

Parasites and Diseases

Throughout the course of the Blue-winged Teal research a close check was kept on migrating and resident birds to ascertain losses from parasites and diseases. Dead or sick birds were infrequently found, and there were no epidemics observed. Most of the dead and sick birds were found to have been suffering from some injury inflicted by causes other than by parasites and diseases (mechanical injuries, page 114).

LICE

Two species of lice were recorded from the Blue-winged Teal during the course of the five-year period. They were: *Anataecus dentatus* and *Trinotum querquedulae.* Fully 80 percent of the teal was infested with one or more species of lice. The identifications of the lice were made by Dr. Robert L. Roudabush, Zoology and Entomology Department, Iowa State College.

WORMS

Practically all young ducks examined in the Ruthven area had a few round worms, flukes or tapeworms present in their alimentary tract. No deaths were attributed to these parasites.

LEECHES

Mr. Clarence Sooter, graduate assistant, Zoology and Entomology Department, Iowa State College, found leeches *(Theromyzon occidentalis)* infesting young waterfowl in the Ruthven area during the summer of 1936 (Sooter, 1937). Four out of six Blue-winged Teal ducklings were found infested with the leech. At this time the author is unable to state the severity of such parasitism.

MALARIA-LIKE DISEASE

The malaria-like disease of ducks as found in Michigan (O'Roke, 1934) was not observed in the Iowa marshes. The Ruthven area apparently was not conducive to the propagation of the vector, black flies *(Simulium* spp.*)*. Approximately 60 blood smears were made from Iowa ducks (Blue-winged Teal, pintail and Shoveller) and examined. No evidence was obtained that showed the presence of the malaria-like parasite *(Leucocytozoön anatis)* in the blood of any of the ducks examined.

BOTULISM

Botulism, caused by the bacillus *(Clostridium botulinus)* was not found affecting ducks in the research area.

LEAD POISONING

Three Blue-winged Teal, suffering from lead poisoning, were observed over the five-year period in the Ruthven area. The three birds were found during the spring migration of 1934. The soft, boggy bottoms of the Iowa marshes eliminate most of the chances of ducks picking up shot. It is entirely possible that the shot was picked up before the birds reached the Ruthven area.

CHAPTER XV

Agriculture and Drainage

There are approximately 35,856,000 acres of land in the State of Iowa. Prior to 1900 about 6,000,000 acres of land in the state were tall grass prairie, heavily interspersed with thousands of potholes and marshes. Practically each 40-acre tract had at least one pothole. In general it can be said that the 6,000,000 acres were used by waterfowl for nesting or rearing purposes during the spring and summer. Fig. 28, of Dickinson County (taken in part from rail map, Elwell and Boatman, 1923) illustrates the extent of water areas in northern Iowa in the past and in the present. Before the disruption of that great waterfowl habitat the State of Iowa probably produced between three million and four million ducks yearly (chiefly Blue-winged Teal, Shoveller, mallard, Redhead, Ruddy Duck and pintail).

The first settlers in northern Iowa farmed and cultivated the high upland prairies, not attempting to drain the potholes and marshes. Later (about 1900) the state became recognized as rich in soil of the highest types. The yields of crops and the prices on the prairies encouraged engineers to work out methods of drainage for the potholes and marshes to further advance grain production in the state. The coming of the World War in 1914 opened up outlets for products that could be raised on the prairies. That great catastrophe added impetus to the drainage program. By 1920 the greater part of the 6,000,000 acres was classified as drained land. The potholes and marshes became corn-producing land that sold for as much as $500 per acre shortly after the War. Iowa became the richest agricultural state in the United States. Today Iowa has left approximately 50,000 acres of scattered marshes and potholes that remind us of what once existed. On those acres the Blue-winged Teal has remained with us.

Not more than 5 percent of the marshes drained proved to be unproductive crop land. The only regret is that more was not known concerning drainage and drained soils at the time

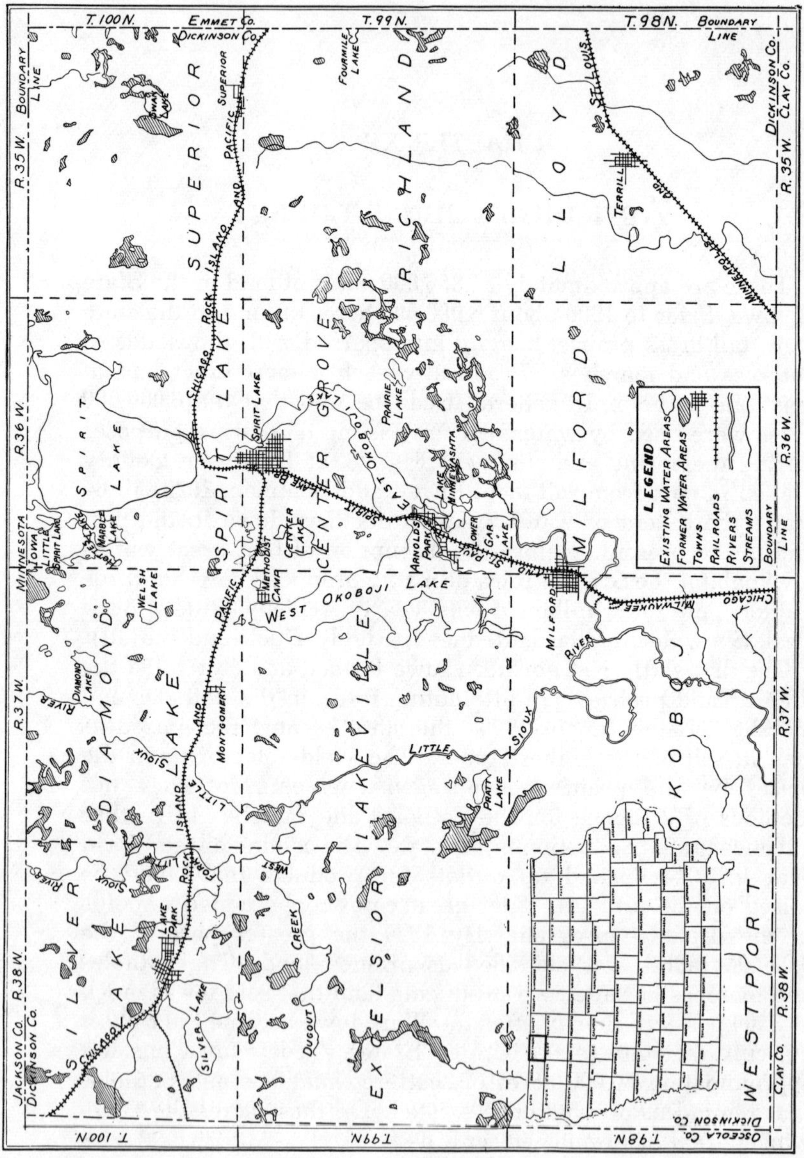

FIG. 28. Dickinson County, Iowa. The shaded region on the map represent water areas over 10 acres in size that have been drained since 1900.

FIG. 29. *(left)* The emergent vegetation of a pothole trampled and overgrazed by cattle. (Photo by P. A. DuMont.) FIG. 30. *(right)* Squirrel-tail grass as a dominant in the wet meadow brought about by overgrazing. (Photo by H. H. Knight.)

the drainage was carried out. The 5 percent that was failure would have left Iowa a fine distribution of lakes, sloughs, potholes and marshes that would today be worth millions of dollars in terms of recreation and water conservation.

LAND USE PRACTICES

This discussion on land use practices will deal only with that agricultural land adjoining water areas. Those acres that produce 30-60 bushels of corn per acre adjoining marshes are probably serving their best purpose. Hence, the acreages not producing high value crops is the basis for the following discussion.

Grazing. The nesting margins of most of the marshes and potholes are not drained well enough to allow cultivation on a profitable basis. About 40 percent of the margins is grazed by cattle, horses and sheep each year. Cattle are by far the dominant grazing animals. The number of sheep held by Iowa farmers may vary greatly from year to year. Sheep were grazed on the margin of only one marsh in the Ruthven area each spring and summer during the course of the research period. About 5 percent of the grazing animals was horses.

Overgrazing can very easily eliminate nesting Blue-winged Teal from an area. In 1933 overgrazing and drought together practically evicted all nesting Blue-winged Teal in about one-half of the marsh areas in northwest Iowa. That condition was brought about by several factors in addition to the two main causes named above. The effects of the drought were first felt in the western range states. Thousands of western drought-stricken cattle were shipped into Iowa and sold at very low prices. The number of cattle placed in the Ruthven area pastures just about doubled in the short space of a month, June 15-July 15, 1933. The drought became serious in Iowa and pastures generally suffered greatly. The carrying capacity of pastures margining the marshes in normal years in Iowa is about one cow per two acres. The drought cut the carrying capacity fully 75 percent. Where the pastures should have been carrying one cow per nine acres they were grazed by about one cow per two acres after the influx of western cattle.

What happened? The grasses were eaten, trampled and burned out in many pastures. There was no place for a teal to build a nest. Cattle in some areas were forced to eat the bulrushes (rearing cover and food) in the marsh proper (fig. 29).

Disregarding the plight of the pastures and the ducks in the fall of 1933, most of the cattle were sold at a good profit. The profits earned in the fall on the cattle were by no means net profits. The following spring, instead of grasses being the dominant plants revegetating the pastures, lesser ragweed, hoary vervain, blue vervain and squirrel-tail grass were the dominants. (Not one teal nest was found in a pure stand of the weed plants.) These plants are all low in forage value and unattractive to nesting teal. On the upland meadows bluegrass was supplanted by lesser ragweed, hoary vervain and blue vervain. The wet meadows normally grown up to bluegrass and slough grass grew up to squirrel-tail grass in 1934 (fig. 30).

Squirrel-tail grass, in addition to being low in forage value, causes painful wounds to grazing animals. The barbs of the achenes pierce the lips, tongue, throat and nostrils of the animals. Three years later, 1936, many of the areas overgrazed in 1933 could not support over one cow per eight acres. In the end the farmers and the teal suffered.

GRAZING EXPERIMENT

Dewey's Pasture, a bluegrass tract of 392 acres, Clay County, Iowa, was purchased by the Iowa Fish and Game Commission during the summer of 1934. This tract lies adjacent to Mud Lake, which is privately owned. Within the 392 acres are 44 potholes, ranging from one-quarter acre to eight acres in size. The distribution of potholes in relation to surrounding duck nesting cover creates an ideal Blue-winged Teal nesting area (Bennett, 1935).

The author began duck nesting studies in the area in 1933, one year before the tract was purchased by the state. The duck nesting population and mammals have been carefully observed in the pasture each year since 1933.

In 1933, 85 head of cattle grazed the area from the last of May to September 15. In that year there were on the area 37 successful Blue-winged Teal nests, two Mallard nests, two Pintail nests and one Shoveller nest.

Three striped skunk dens were found in the pasture. A normal rainfall insured the vegetation against overgrazing by the 85 cattle.

In 1934 Iowa witnessed a severe drought. The hot winds and lack of rains burned out much of the bluegrass in the pasture. In its place grew lesser ragweed, hoary vervain and goldenrod. Drought-stricken cattle were shipped in from the west and sold to Iowa farmers at low prices shortly before the drought was felt in the state. The manager of the pasture in that year placed 175 cattle in the area for grazing purposes, some of which were low-priced drought-stricken cattle. The entire pasture was severely overgrazed as a result. All duck nests, those of eight Blue-winged Teal, were destroyed because of lack of cover (trampling by cattle and by predators). There was one active skunk den and one active badger den found in the pasture that summer. The area was purchased by the state that summer, but the cattle grazing contract could not be canceled until the close of the grazing season.

The spring of 1935 found the area free of cattle. Nearly normal rainfall gave the bluegrass and some of the prairie plants an excellent chance to survive and flourish. Most of the lesser ragweeds and vervain were crowded out by bluegrass. However, the drought of the year before caused about one-third of the potholes to remain dry. During the nesting season 28 Blue-winged Teal nests, 1 Mallard nest and 1 Shoveller nest were found. Two of the duck nests were destroyed by striped skunks. By the end of the grazing season about 13 skunk dens and 2 badger dens were located.

With continued protection from grazing in 1936, the area grew up into a mat of grasses. The new vegetation, mostly bluegrass, grew up to 18 inches with a mat of old grasses underneath. The vegetation was so dense that ducklings, after hatching, probably had difficulty in walking from the nest to water. Thirty-three Blue-winged Teal nests, 2 mallard nests and 2 Shoveller nests were found. Four duck nests were destroyed by skunks and two duck nests were pilfered by badgers. Approximately 40 skunk dens and 4 badger dens were found that summer. Table XVII shows the data tabulated for the four-year period.

FIG. 31. The inlet of a marsh denuded by hogs. Each freshet carries tons of soil into the water area.

TABLE XVII. *Dewey's pasture—392 acres*

Extent of grazing	1933 Moderately grazed	1934 Overgrazed	1935 No grazing	1936 No grazing
Cattle	85	175	0	0
Duck nests	42	8	30	37
Skunk dens	3	1	13	40
Duck nests destroyed by skunks	0	0	2	4
Badger dens	0	1	2	4
Duck nests destroyed by badgers	0	0	0	2

The Blue-winged Teal, the most common nesting duck in Iowa, builds its nest almost invariably on dry land in the grasses. The average distance of a nest from water is about 40 yards. The little ducklings walk to the water shortly after they hatch. From observations (previously described, page 52) the author has noticed that the mother teal leads her young from the nest down old roads, cow paths and other open areas where the young do not have to overexert themselves. During 1933, in Dewey's Pasture, the 85 cattle grazed open spaces and made paths for the youngsters to get to water without a great deal of struggle. By 1936 the protected vegetation had become so rank that the young evidently were forced to traverse almost impassable barriers of plant growth.

Another aspect to the protection of the pasture from grazing was the increase of skunks and badgers along with the development of the vegetation. The fall of 1936 found a very high population of skunks in the area. Some parts of the pasture were literally dug up by skunks in their feeding activities. Such a skunk population could very easily cause much nest destruction. The data (Table XVII) show that the increase of skunks was evidenced by an increased number of skunk-destroyed nests.

TABLE XVIII. *Area A—20 acres*

Extent of grazing	1933 Capacity grazed	1934 Over-grazed	1935 Capacity grazed	1936 Over-grazed
Cattle	8	7	10	11
Duck nests	1	0	1	1
Skunk dens	0	0	0	0
Badger dens	0	0	0	0

Several pastures within one mile of Dewey's Pasture furnished check data. One pasture, Area A (Table XVIII) of 20 acres was grazed each year at the rate of one cow per two to three acres. Such grazing in the drought years, 1934 and 1936, reduced the grazing capacity to nil by mid-August both years. One Blue-winged Teal nest was found each year in 1933, 1935 and 1936. There were neither skunk nor badger dens present during the periods of observation.

Check Area B, a bluegrass tract of 110 acres, was grazed by one cow per four to five acres throughout the four-year period. With the exception of 1934 the area supported one Blue-winged Teal nest per 10 acres each year (Table XIX). There was an increase in skunk and badger populations in the pasture but the increase was slight as compared with that in Dewey's Pasture.

Can a duck nesting margin be pastured? The data presented bring out some rather complicated factors. By checking back to Dewey's Pasture in 1933 (Table XVII) it seems as though a certain amount of grazing (1 cow per 4.6 acres) was beneficial

FIG. 32. A neighboring marsh with a slough grass grown inlet. Very little soil washes into the marsh.

TABLE XIX. *Area—100 acres*

Extent of grazing	1933 Moderately grazed	1934 Overgrazed	1935 Moderately grazed	1936 Moderately grazed
Cattle	21	23	27	18
Duck nests	12	3	10	9
Skunk dens	0	0	2	3
Badger dens	0	0	0	1
Duck nests destroyed by skunk or badger	0	0	0	0

to nesting ducks Check Area A, with capacity grazing, one cow per two acres, supported one duck nest per 20 acres each year with the exception of 1934. Check Area B, with moderate grazing, supported one duck nest per 10 acres with the exception of 1934.

Dewey's Pasture in 1935 and 1936, in an ungrazed condition, supported one duck nest per 12 acres. In addition, Dewey's Pasture in 1935 and 1936 harbored a skunk and badger population that showed evidence of being a factor in duck nest destruction. After all, the same area was grazed by bison *(Bison bison)* a century ago. It is known that the area was a waterfowl paradise at that time. Each animal in its natural state must have played a part in balancing nature. Thus, it seems as though grazing to a certain extent is needed, even today. Light grazing apparently destroyed the ideal skunk and badger habitat in the study area. (There was an increase in skunk and badger populations over the state, 1933-36, but the increase in Dewey's Pasture was abnormal; the increase in Area B indicated more nearly the actual statewide trend.)

Pastures can be safely grazed, from a pasture standpoint, in normal years in northwest Iowa one cow per two acres. In drought years pastures may be reduced below any carrying capacity by midsummer. From all observations to date the indications are that one cow per six acres in normal years is beneficial to the duck nesting areas in Iowa. The state can obtain at least $5 per head for the grazing period on the state-owned nesting margins. Dewey's Pasture, 392 acres minus 50 acres of water, would support about 57 cattle, netting the state $285. This income would pay the upkeep expenses, such as fence repair and the construction of earthen dams at the outlets of the potholes.

WILD HAY AS A CROP

Slough grass, known as wild hay, was harvested each year in the Ruthven area on about 40 percent of the marshes. In years of feed shortage the hay sold for as much as $12 per ton. Other years it sold at $3-$6 per ton for packing (used for packing glassware, pottery and other breakables) and feed purposes. In years of normal rainfall one to two tons of hay per acre could be harvested. Cutting operations began in June and July. There is no set time or condition for the harvest as in the reaping of alfalfa. The harvest is usually done when other farm work allows it. When the hay is cut in June a large percentage of teal nests is destroyed. If mowing is delayed until July 1, about 95 percent of the live nests escapes the mower. Where farming conditions permit, the conservation-minded farmer could withhold mowing operations until July 1 and insure himself of a crop of hay, pheasants and teal.

Wild hay has other uses that are utilized knowingly and unknowingly, sometimes profitably and sometimes unprofitably. It is a cattle food, a soil holder and a water holder.

In Iowa the number of lakes is small. The rich land in their water sheds is cultivated. This condition causes much silting. Many of the present open water lakes are becoming marshes and the marshes in turn are becoming upland, hastened at an alarming rate by cultivated water sheds. First of all, then, from a national and state standpoint, in relation to a soil-holding program and from a water conservation standpoint, all land surrounding the marshes and lakes should be utilized to its greatest extent for the welfare of the people.

Slough grass can be, and in some cases is, being utilized to its greatest extent by saving lakes, providing yearly yields of hay and nesting cover for pheasants and ducks. Many of the inlets to marshes and margin of marshes in Iowa are denuded of vegetation by hogs and cattle, allowing tons of black soil to fill up the water areas (fig. 31). Those denuded areas return but little to the farmer and take much from him. An area as in fig. 32, grown up to slough grass, could produce a yearly crop of hay and save the marsh. Water was about all the hogs were getting in the area. A similar inlet to another marsh is shown in fig. 32. This tract is providing feed for cattle, conserving soil and water, saving the marsh and providing nesting cover for pheasant and teal The proper utilization of many marshes and marsh margins is conducive to the production of Blue-winged Teal.

CHAPTER XVI

Breeding, Refuge, and Shooting Areas

Once the initiative for the establishment of a waterfowl restoration project has been generated, public wildlife officials, shooting clubs, conservation organizations and individuals are immedately confronted with the problem of choosing and financing the purchase of a favorable site for the production of ducks. The first act that an organization or individual should do is to find out through ornithological records, game officials or old residents if the species of duck nested commonly in the region in the past. In the prairie states there are still many remnants of marsh areas that could be restored more easily and more cheaply than by picking out a completely drained marsh or an upland area and converting it into a marsh. In many of the remaining marshes teal still nest. The presence of the birds under adverse conditions is an excellent indication that an early success will be achieved upon restoration properly carried out.

An area might be purchased in Illinois for $40 per acre and not produce any ducks at all, while an area in South Dakota at $5 per acre might produce near the maximum number of ducks. Or, a marshy tract in one section of Iowa at say $60 per acre might produce ten times the number of ducks as a similar tract at say $10 per acre in another part of the state. Thus, in choosing an area for restoration or management the initial cost must not be the deciding factor in the purchase of land.

The prairie habitat seems to furnish ideal breeding conditions for the Blue-winged Teal (fig. 33). The small number of predatory species, abundance of nesting cover, abundance of rearing cover and the abundance of food found on the prairie, all combine to create favorable conditions for this small duck. Thus, the teal production area should be situated in the prairie area for maximum production.

The forest water areas are used during migration to a great extent, but only a small percentage of teal is produced in such areas. The Mississippi River is a good example of the timbered type of breeding areas in Iowa (fig. 34). Very few teal nest along the Mississippi River. The following data (Table XX) present a number of reasons why the teal may prefer the prairies to the timbered water areas.

The timbered tracts have but little nesting cover for teal and in addition support a number of animals that are known to be destroyers of ground nesting birds and their young. Thus,

TABLE XX. *Comparison of prairie and timbered habitats*

Iowa Prairies—Clay County, Iowa, 1935	Comparisons	Mississippi River Country, McGregor, Iowa, 1935
few	trees	dominant
few	shrubs	abundant
dominant	grasses (nesting cover)	few
few	snapping turtles	abundant
rare	soft-shell turtle	abundant
rare	blue racer	common
rare	bull snake	abundant
rare	black snake	common
rare	fox snake	common
few	Great Horned Owl	common
few	crows	abundant
few	red fox	common
not present	gray fox	common
few	coyote	rare
common	mink	common
rare	raccoon	common
common	striped skunk	common
few	spotted skunk	common
common	badger	rare

in picking an area for production it would be well to select the type of habitat that seems to be favorable to the species in question. The Mississippi River tracts should probably be managed for Wood Duck *(Aix sponsa)*, Eastern Ruffed Grouse *(Bonasa umbellus umbellus)*, Eastern Bob-white and fur bearers, but apparently not for the production of Blue-winged Teal.

Of the teal nests observed not one nest was found in cover beneath trees. Nor was a nest found in or under shrubs. In the Ruthven area, bordering some of the marshes, were found stands of bur oak *(Quercus macrocarpa)*. Although the adja-

FIG. 33. *(left)* A typical prairie pothole. FIG. 34. *(right)* The upper Mississippi River at McGregor, Iowa. (Photo by Tom Scott.)

cent water area supported ideal food and rearing cover the teal did not nest under or within 80 yards of the trees. Incidentally, it was in those tracts that a few Great Horned Owls and crows were found. Also, the trees replaced the valuable grasses needed for nesting cover. Willows (*Salix* spp.) did not have such a deleterious effect upon the nesting ducks. A number of nests were found within 20 feet of willows but none under them. The willows, like the oaks, crowded out the grasses (fig. 35).

Snowberry *(Symphoricarpos racemosus)* was found persisting in small quarter acre patches in some of the prairie areas. No teal nests were found in or under this shrub (fig. 36). The patches of snowberry in a majority of cases harbored the dens of striped skunks or badgers. In two patches coyotes had dug their dens. Good grassy cover was also absent under the shrub.

Desirable size of water areas. Throughout the course of the waterfowl studies the author had the opportunity to observe large numbers of sloughs, marshes and potholes. Frequently on small sloughs and potholes the number of ducks and ducklings was much larger in proportion to the water area than on larger marshes or sloughs. The pothole duck nesting country of the prairie regions has been known for many years to have been one of the greatest, if not the greatest, duck-producing area in the world. It was naturally assumed that this was because of the many water areas with an abundant supply of food and cover. Why should the pothole areas produce more ducks than large sloughs or marshes? It was found that 95.6 percent of the puddle ducks nested within 220 yards of the shoreline of marsh, slough or pothole, regardless of the size of such water area (see p. 46). Thereby a relationship between shoreline length and the usable amount of nesting cover became evident. As an example, let one figure the comparative shoreline lengths on a marsh approximately a mile square and on a marsh one mile wide and two miles long. The smaller marsh would have a shoreline of four miles and the larger marsh would have a shoreline of six miles, although twice the size of the smaller marsh. If each marsh had a 220-yard nesting margin, the smaller marsh would have 360 acres of usable nesting area to 640 acres of water as against 520 acres of usable nesting area to 1,320 acres of water for the large marsh. Another example would be of two marshes of the same water area but different in shape. Suppose a marsh to be 1 mile wide and 10 miles long. The shoreline mileage would be about 22 miles, and with a 220-yard margin of usable nesting ground the marsh would have 1,800 acres of nesting area. The other marsh of the same water area but one-half mile wide and 20 miles long would have 41 miles of shoreline with 3,320 acres of nesting area. Theoretically, if each nesting margin were carrying equal numbers of nests per margin acre, the long narrow marsh would produce 86 percent more ducks than the other marsh of the same water acreage. By using the same principle on potholes down to one-half acre in size it becomes evident why a pothole

TABLE XXI. *Brood counts on potholes from Prince Albert, Saskatchewan*

Number of potholes	Size (acres)	Number of broods	Total acreage	Acres per brood
16	½	3	8	2.6
30	1	7	30	4.2
19	2	9	38	4.2
10	3	8	30	3.7
8	4	6	32	5.3
4	5	2	20	10
4	6	3	24	8
3	8	3	24	8
4	10	4	40	10
1	12	1	12	12

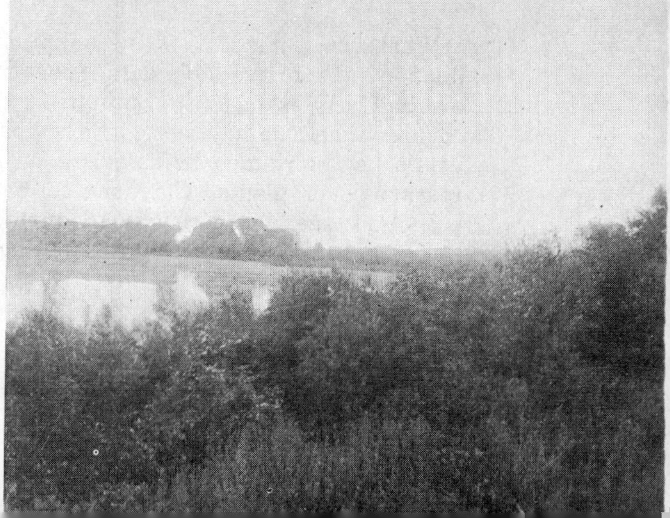

FIG. 35. Willows invading the upland margin. These growths eliminate the grasses needed for nest cover. (Photo by H. H. Knight.)

produces more ducks per acre of water than potholes and marshes of larger size.

O. C. Furniss (1935) made a survey of the numbers of duck broods seen on 99 potholes on 16 quarter-sections of land near Prince Albert, Saskatchewan. The area examined was pothole country, the size of potholes ranging from one-half acre to 12 acres (Table XXI). The author during the years of 1932-36 made similar counts on marshes in northwest Iowa (Table XXII). These data on varying sizes of water areas substantiate the principle set forth that the ratio of shoreline to the water area has a definite relationship to the amount of usable nesting area.

TABLE XXII. *Brood counts on water areas from Northwest Iowa*

Number of water areas	Size (acres)	Number of broods	Total acreage	Acres per brood
11	½	3	5.5	1.8
161	1	43	161	3.7
26	2	12	52	4.3
7	3	4	21	5.2
13	4	4	52	13
6	5	4	30	7.5
7	8	6	56	9.3
3	10	3	30	10
10	15	12	150	12.5
9	18	12	162	13.5
4	20	7	80	11.4
6	30	13	180	13.8
4	40	18	160	8.9
2	65	16	130	8.1
3	80	21	240	11.4
6	120	51	720	14.1
4	200	97	800	8.2
9	250	114	2,250	19.7
8	400	120	3,200	26.6

What size water area is the optimum for puddle duck production? From available data it seems as though a pothole of one-half acre is near the optimum. The suitability of areas smaller than one-half acre in size for maximum production would be determined by sufficient water depths for food and rearing cover plants. Care should be taken when restoring potholes to see that there is an adequate number of larger water areas in the region to accommodate ducklings and ducks when the dry periods of summer tend to dry up the smaller water areas.

Manipulation of water levels. The availability of water and ease with which it may be held is of vital importance in selecting an area for restoration. A semidrained marsh at $50 per acre is much more desirable than a drained or upland area at $5 per acre where the construction of long dikes and retaining walls might run up an additional cost of $80 per acre. Many semidrained marshes and drought-affected sloughs can be made to hold water by the construction of low-cost earthen dams or by the plugging of tile outlets. In every case where restoration is planned a competent engineer should be consulted as to the practicability of the project from the standpoints of finance and feasibility.

After an area has been selected for restoration the next important steps are proper conservation of water and manipulation of its level. The water depth is directly responsible for the rearing cover and food plants. Most of the desirable puddle duck foods and rearing cover in Iowa flourish at water depths from two to five feet. As the prairie marsh has a bottom of rather uniform topography, with little fall, it is not difficult to maintain a rather even depth over the entire marsh.

Several years ago the water level of an ideal duck marsh, Rush Lake, Palo Alto County, Iowa, was raised from a level of four feet to a level of seven feet. The following year the marsh became an open water lake. Now, few ducks visit the lake at any time. None nests there. The muskrats and other marsh inhabitants have vanished. The lake does provide some bullhead (*Ameiurus* spp.) fishing, but it is no longer suitable for waterfowl. Many people in that locality attributed the disappearance of the emergent vegetation and the submerged duck foods to some phenomenon, surely not the result of their own doings.

Before the drainage era in Iowa the northern half of the state was heavily dotted with hundreds of potholes and marshes. Because of plant succession those water areas were of varying depths. The more shallow ones dried up each summer, often during the rearing season. The proximity of deeper water areas probably then as now saved the ducklings of those dry areas. The desirability of potholes and small marsh areas in the immediate vicinity of a large marsh make the entire area attractive to larger numbers of teal and as a result a greater production occurs in such areas. Small water areas out on the prairie make available much more nesting cover. A marsh one-

FIG. 36. Snowberry becoming the dominant plant in an upland margin. This shrub is not attractive to the Blue-winged Teal as nesting cover.

quarter of a mile wide and two miles long has 50 percent more margin than an area of the same size, one-half mile wide and one mile long. Thus, the more potholes and small marshes the greater the percentage of nesting margins. However, as stated before, it is necessary to have some larger and deeper marshes in a pothole area to take care of the ducks when the smaller areas dry up in the middle of the summer.

In many of the areas in Iowa numerous potholes would be formed naturally by the restoration of a drained, drought-stricken marsh. The construction of low-cost earthen dams at the outlets of potholes and sloughs helps greatly in holding water over the summer period. Such dams aid particularly in maintaining water for young coots and grebes. These birds, unlike the teal ducklings, are poor walkers and will often remain to die in the dried-up areas.

Nesting cover. It was found that a margin 220 yards wide around a water area was sufficient for 95 percent of the nesting ducks. It would probably be impossible or impractical in many cases to try to locate every pothole or marsh in a formation among other water areas in such a way as to provide a 220-yard margin for each water area. This could be carried out on isolated water areas and on many potholes but there would be many potholes and marshes close together prohibiting such wide margins.

In Iowa corn land extends to within 20 yards of some of the marshes (fig. 37). In such instances a 50-yard margin would be of great value to ducks and at the same time would eliminate the high cost of purchasing the adjoining agricultural land.

The margin, if grown up to bluegrass, could be grazed in normal years from June 1 to September 1 at the rate of one cow per six acres without injury to the nesting ducks (p. 102). Grazing to that extent, as far as the author can ascertain at present, is beneficial and not detrimental to a nesting area. The income from the sale of grazing rights might well be used for the upkeep of fences, dams and other management needs.

If the margin of the marsh is grown up to slough grass, some years the sale of it as hay will net an income that may be used on the upkeep of the area. Mowing should be delayed until after July 1. In years when the price of wild hay is not conducive to making the vegetation can be left standing as winter cover for pheasants and prairie chickens.

Islands have long been known as favorite nesting retreats in some areas. Islands represent a concentrated margin effect. Thus, with hundreds of acres of water having islands suitable for nesting, a concentration of nesting birds is sometimes found on them. In Iowa, where margins of marshes are not bordered by trees or shrubs, nesting on the whole is greater than on islands.

Rearing cover. In Iowa the key to success for having suitable rearing cover is adequate water depth. The peatlike soil of the prairie region is conducive to rank growths of round-stemmed bulrushes, river bulrush, cat-tail, reed, bur-reed, arrowheads, smartweeds and sedges, all of which contribute excellent rearing habitats. These plants propagate abundantly in water one to five feet deep. Most of the marshes in Iowa should have from four to five feet of water during the month of May so that evaporation during a normal summer will not lower the water to a depth less than one or two feet.

FIG. 37. *(left)* A cornfield extending to the water's edge of a marsh. Such cultivation eliminates nesting possibilities. FIG. 38. *(right)* Telephone wires across the narrows of two marshes. (Bank swallows *(Riparia riparia riparia)* on wires.)

In addition to their value for ducks, cover plants are essential for muskrats. These fur bearers thrive in such marshes and the work by them can be classified as beneficial to ducks. The openings made by feeding and house building activity of muskrats create ideal feeding areas for adult and young teal. The decomposed muskrat houses grown up to vegetation furnish roosting and hiding places for the ducklings and adults. The old and unused houses make ideal waiting sites for the breeding males in the spring. The taking of surplus muskrats each year protects the marsh from overfeeding by muskrats and the income from the sale of their furs may be used to defray the expenses of the breeding area.

Food. Food plants, like cover plants, require certain water depths to thrive. Nature has made it possible for cover plants and food plants to grow in the same aquatic habitat. The duck food plants of the prairie marsh grow abundantly in water one to five feet deep, the same depth at which the cover plants propagate.

Many of the cover plants, such as the bulrushes, smartweeds and bur-reeds serve also as food plants. Also, many of the food plants such as duck potato and smartweeds contribute rearing cover.

Insects, snails and crustaceans that are eaten by ducks thrive in the same rush-grown waters. Maintaining a proper water level over the prairie marshes in Iowa is the greatest single factor in food production.

Thousands of dollars have been spent by well-meaning sportsmen for the purchase of duck foods for restocking purposes. In one instance the author was invited by a conservation organization to aid in the planting of purchased duck foods in a duck marsh. In this case $200 had been spent for the purchase of sago pondweed seeds and tubers. The planting party arrived at the marsh on the arranged date and began to row a boat out into the marsh. Rank growths of submerged "weeds" made rowing almost impossible. After much laboring one of the paddlers inquired of me, "How can we get rid of these weeds in our marsh?" I calmly replied, "Oh! That is sago pondweed." This group of well-meaning sportsmen did not know what sago pondweed looked like and took it for granted that their marsh was short of duck foods. If the $200 had been spent for the protection of nesting cover around the marsh during the nesting season, many ducks would have been produced.

Nesting cover was the only requirement that the marsh lacked for duck production

The author has not observed a marsh, slough or pothole in Iowa that needed a restocking of duck foods. True, some water areas were short of food and rearing cover, but the scarcity was due to improper water depths or infertile bottoms. Repeated plantings in such areas have not remedied the situation.

Marshes that have been drained for years, marshes temporarily dry due to drought, permanent marshes and restored marshes in the prairie area as a general rule do not need artificial restocking. Dormant seeds, wind-blown seeds, water carried tubers and seeds, and animal-carried seeds and tubers rapidly rehabilitate a marsh with vegetation once the proper water level has been restored. The insects, snails and crustaceans increase along with vegetative development.

REFUGE AREAS

Protection. Perhaps the greatest value of refuge is protection to migratory waterfowl during the fall migration. In most states the acreage of "shootable waters" is at least several thousand times that of refuge areas. It is the duty of those sections of the country that are favored with migrating ducks to guarantee an adequate return of breeding stock to the nesting grounds each year. To do this every water area cannot be shot and at the same time perpetuate and increase these birds of sport.

The hunters of Iowa probably take at least ten times the number of ducks that are produced within the state. Would it not be unethical if the sportsmen of each state did not insure the protection of a reasonable percentage of the ducks to go through unharmed for breeding purposes? Theoretically it may be that one refuge-acre per each shooting-acre will be necessary to perpetuate the sport. Further studies of the yearly kill, crippling losses, yearly production and diseases and hazards may eventually give the correct shooting area-refuge area ratio.

Location of refuge. The greatest need for refuges is in those areas that concentrate the migrating birds. Bottlenecks of lake regions, mouths of rivers and isolated water areas that are required by long-distance flying birds are perhaps the situations in which the greatest hazard of over-shooting occurs. In northwestern Iowa in Clay, Palo Alto, Dickinson and Emmet Counties the swamps and lakes represent the southern tip of a series of water areas in eastern South Dakota and western Minnesota. Thousands of ducks are forced into that limited area each fall. On the opening day of the shooting season in 1936 the marshes in that region averaged one duck hunter per acre. The state maintains 31 public shooting areas in that region as against three refuges. But are three refuges adequate in such a concentration area? Perhaps the restoration of semidrained areas into shooting areas and equal number of refuges would relieve the concentrated shooting and give greater protection to the birds.

Water levels. The water level of a refuge should be of a depth conducive to the growth of food plants. Abnormally large numbers of ducks are forced to utilize those havens of safety and as a result a greater food supply is needed. Many deep-water lake refuges serve only as resting areas and the birds have to go to shooting areas for food. The breeding ground marsh that holds water throughout the year makes an ideal refuge. The shallow waters and the rich growth of food plants are ideal safety habitats for the Blue-winged Teal.

Hazards. There are several hazards around most of the concentration areas in Iowa that could be eliminated or avoided at little cost with a great saving of duck life. Telephone wires are found crossing many of the main passes in the lake region (fig. 38). Roads usually are built between the narrows of lakes along which are placed telephone and electric wires. These wire obstructions are in many cases only a danger to flying birds for a matter of a few yards, but on days of low visibility large numbers of ducks are killed. Mortality from this cause goes on in the fall, spring and summer. Certainly a refuge should not have such an instrument of death strung across its acres. In many instances the wires could be enclosed in a conduit along the road bed or on the bottom of the marsh.

The object of a refuge is to give protection from as many causes of mortality as possible. A refuge should have a protective margin of at least 200 yards to prevent the shooting of incoming and outgoing ducks. Sorry to relate, in many states the state does not own any land surrounding its water areas. In Iowa a riparian water right law gives the adjacent land owner complete jurisdiction over land up to the water's edge. As a result many refuges are surrounded to the water's edge by commercial duck hunting enterprises. In Iowa the usual price ranges from fifty cents to one dollar per day for shooting rights. Fortunately the ducks soon learn to come in and to go out at high altitudes beyond the range of shotguns. However, on stormy days when the visibility is poor the ducks are forced to fly well within a killing range. More shooting areas and more refuges would probably lessen the concentration of shooting around refuges and increase their value in conformity with the purpose for which they were established. Where possible, in particularly poor agricultural land, the state should purchase a protective margin for refuges. The pass shooting on refuge boundaries results in thousands of crippled birds that fly into the refuge to die.

The poisoning of ducks by lead shot is known to take a toll throughout the United States and other countries where shooting is done. One shot seems to be a lethal dose for some ducks, whereas others may take several hundred before succumbing. In Iowa very few ducks have been found or reported as dying from this cause. Most of Iowa's duck areas have muck bottoms and the ducks do not have a chance to pick up the shot. A hard-packed sandy- or clay-bottomed water area is an ideal situation for ducks to gather up the shot. Forcing ducks into hard-bottomed lakes posted as refuges that have been shot over for years is worse than no refuge at all. Forcing ducks into areas contaminated with botulism under the guise of refuges should also be condemned.

Predators and fur bearers. Under ordinary conditions there are many wounded birds that will not recover and which provide more than enough food for predatory species found on the refuge. Predatory species have little effect upon migratory ducks on the Iowa marshes. The disturbance caused by control practices would be too disrupting on a refuge during the flights to warrant the trouble.

The yearly reaping of surplus muskrats on refuges is to be encouraged. Surplus rats may eliminate too much cover and food for the good of the refuge. The income derived from the sale of furs can greatly reduce the cost of upkeep on such areas.

SHOOTING AREAS

Selection of area. A shooting area, as the title suggests, should provide conditions attractive to ducks. In general the water area should have the same essentials as the rearing ground marsh. Those requirements attractive to ducks may be listed as follows:

1. Cover (bulrushes, cat-tails, reeds).
2. Food (pondweeds, duck potato, coontail, etc.).
3. Shallow waters (for dabbling feeding habits).

Whether the water area is of five acres or of several hundred acres, its attractiveness depends upon the presence of the above constituents. The proper manipulation or conservation of water ordinarily insures those conditions. A year-round water depth of two to five feet is conducive to the growth of desirable food and cover plants if the soil of the bottom is suitable. The bottoms of the prairie marshes of Iowa, rich in organic matter, require no artificial propagation of waterfowl food plants.

Long dry periods during the summer and droughts sometimes cause the water levels of marsh areas to shrink to depths of a few inches. If low water stages prevail for a year or two, an overproduction of undesirable vegetation may result. Such growths fill in most open water areas and injure the attractiveness of the marsh. One way in which to combat such a situation is to protect and prohibit the trapping of muskrats. These animals, through their feeding and house building, will open up a number of vegetation-free spots over the marsh that are attractive to teal.

During low water stages willows often invade marshy areas. The restoration of water by normal rainfall or artificial methods eliminates such growths in a relatively short time. One marsh under observation that was infested with willows became free of them one year after the normal water depth of four feet was restored. Three years were consumed by the elimination process on another marsh.

Hunting. To get the greatest amount of enjoyment out of a marsh, hunters should not number more than 1 per 10 acres at any time. A concentration of hunters soon drives the birds out of a marsh and the shooting is ruined for everyone. Congested hunting leads to poor sportsmanship and poor skill. Each hunter seems to be afraid that if he does not shoot, even though the duck is 200 yards high, the fellow down the shore will kill the duck. As a result, the shooting is ruined and many high-flying birds are hit, eventually die, and never come to be counted in the bag.

Crippling losses. Opinions as to the magnitude of crippling and other losses incidental to hunting vary exceedingly. Even when beyond any suspicion of bias, they usually have the weakness of being founded on general impressions, on honest though possibly exceptional experiences, or on one-sided data not of the kind to give a true evaluation of game wastage, preventable or unpreventable. Errington and Bennett (1933) obtained crippling loss data that are based on 1,315 ducks killed or wounded by 106 hunters in northwest Iowa during the fall of 1932. Something less than one-fourth of the birds reported as lost were those receiving injuries from which they perhaps recovered; however, the numbers dying later from hits undetected by observers may compensate for this probable error.

Ratios of birds lost to birds bagged are, as might be expected, correlated with the attributes and proficiency of the hunter, his equipment, the environmental conditions under which he shoots, and the habits and physical characteristics of the game itself.

Most of the data are for marsh shooting and are derived from records of 41 hunters who lost 119 out of 406 ducks hit, or 29.3 percent. The skill of individual hunters is well reflected in their percentage of birds lost. As contrasted with a loss of 41.5 percent of 212 birds shot by 35 ordinary hunters, the six who could be termed veterans lost but 16 percent of 194. Marsh shooting is usually done from rush clumps, muskrat houses or from narrow vegetation-grown gravel points a few inches to a couple of feet under water. Transportation is by means of boat or wading. Decoys are not used in the type of hunting to which reference is made, advantage being taken of ducks that happen to fly within range or are brought nearer by vocal or mechanical calling.

Shooting over mechanical decoys is done under about the same conditions as the preceding, except that the birds are much more easily attracted into killing range. The data show that 13 men lost only 10.7 percent of 384 ducks, which low percentage is readily explainable. As a rule, the hunters who use decoys are well-equipped veterans who are not only careful to pick their shots but often get plenty of chances to do so. There is no question that, so far as lost birds are concerned, shooting over decoys is about as economical as any type of shooting, and probably the most so.

Pass shooting losses for 323 ducks shot by 36 hunters ran highest of all. As in the case of marsh hunting, the role of skill in keeping the losses down was evident enough; 26 veterans lost 25.8 percent of 194 birds, whereas 10 hunters of average experience or less lost 77 birds for the 52 they bagged, or 59.7 percent. Pass shooting is generally done on dry elevations between lakes, from the sides and tops of hills adjacent to water areas or from other points of vantage in waterfowl flyways. Birds that fall on cultivated or pastured land are commonly found without undue difficulty. As the birds fly typically fast and high the preponderance of losses are of ducks hit at ranges too far to be brought down dead, but which alight out on the lakes a quarter mile or more from shore.

Shore-walking and jump-shooting losses show all gradations from zero to 71 percent, depending on the skill, experience, equipment and the scruples of the hunter. Two jump-shooters, working a small creek, bagged 10 ducks and lost none; four other hunters walking on lake shores lost 35.5 percent of 110 ducks. If the birds are not shot at only within good range, and if care is taken to drop them only where they can be secured, losses can be held at a negligible figure. If every duck that gets up or comes half-way within shooting distance receives a volley of shot, wherever it is, the wastage may be appalling. Many hunters without dog, boat or boots who are unwilling to strip or get their clothes wet continue to drop bird after bird out on the water where there is no chance of their being washed in or picked up. Indeed, the hunter's personal attitude governs so much the number of dead and crippled ducks he leaves behind him that other factors assume an aspect of trivial consequence.

For duck shooting as a whole, which is done mainly on flyways and in marshes, it appears that about one duck will be lost for every one bagged. This is deserving of consideration by state game departments compiling the figures given in reports required of licensed hunters. A report on the taking of so many ducks for a season does not signify that the return fairly represents that hunter's kill.

It is plain, then, that a good dog is of inestimable assistance in holding down the percentage of cripples escaping. A good dog may be of splendid service in retrieving ducks, particularly when birds have fallen in dense vegetation. This is very true when the fallen birds are only winged and have gained access to tangles of brush, weeds, rushes or reeds. In duck hunting the value of retrieving dogs scarcely needs mention.

The respectability of a number of hunting methods could be raised by the modification or elimination of wasteful practices.

Shooting at out-of-range birds is doubtless the greatest single cause of avoidable losses. On some duck passes practically every flock flying over at a height of 100 to 150 yards draws the fire of the hunters beneath. Occasionally a duck hurtles earthward, chance-struck by a lone pellet in the head or neck. More often a bird leaves the flock and sails off to alight later. At 60 to 80 yards, commonly accepted range by ordinary hunters with 12-gauge guns, there are winged cripples twisting or fluttering down into rank vegetation, birds staggering in the air, gradually losing altitude, birds that go on with hanging legs, birds that fall too far to be found. These are lost, in proportion of six to four retrieved, according to data obtained for this type of shooting.

TABLE XXIII. *Tabular recapitulation of duck hunting loss data*

Type of shooting	Class of shooter	Number of shooters	Ducks shot	Ducks bagged	Ducks lost	Percentage of loss
Marsh	Veterans	6	194	163	31	16
	Average	35	212	124	88	41.5
Decoys	Veterans	13	384	343	41	10.7
Pass	Veterans	26	194	144	50	25.8
	Average	10	129	52	77	59.7
Cornfield	Veterans	10	82	70	12	14.6
Shore-walking and jump	Veterans	2	10	10	0	0.0
shooting	Average	5	110	71	39	35.5

The reasons for out-of-range shooting are many. The hunter may not be experienced enough to judge distance; this being the case he could afford to pace off 30, 40 and 55 yards, and put up objects the size of game birds to note how big they look. He may, because of inability to distinguish between species, become confused by the realtive size of birds, in which event the intelligent thing for him to do is to learn.

The hunter may be unfamiliar with the killing range of firearms. Granted that the range of standard shotguns has been appreciably extended the past few years by improved ammunition, there is still a limit to their effectiveness. Forty yards is still about as far as heavy loads from choke-bored 12-gauge guns can be relied upon to kill, with any regularity, tough game, like overhead drake mallards or straight-away cock pheasant. For side shots or for lighter ducks, hen pheasants, grouse, possibly 10 yards more may be allowable, assuming that gun and loads are correct. Fifty yards with a good gun and the best of loads is far enough to send a shot charge after almost anything, and very often too far, despite ammunition advertisements to the effect that 80 yards is easy.

Perhaps most baneful of all, save indifference, is the popular feeling that successful long shots demonstrate a shooter's superior ability. They do not. It is no trick to encompass a bird at 100 yards with a shot pattern 20 feet across; it is no proud feat to make a "scratch" kill at some impossible distance. Shooting at excessive ranges denotes not expert skill but the very opposite. It is almost certain that beginners in any hunting crowd can be recognized by their propensity for shooting at anything; the veterans seldom shoot unless they are sure of their birds, then kill cleanly.

Competitive shooting, as by massed gunners along main duck flights, may force one to shoot at high birds if he hopes to get any at all. To this there does not seem to be an adequate answer. Everyone loses, the game included, except insofar as the birds are educated by the bombardment to fly habitually at higher levels. Under such circumstances a discriminating sportsman has not much alternative save to go elsewhere, home if there is nowhere else to go. Certainly little that could be called sport is to be had by remaining.

While it is a good general policy to shoot sparingly in the course of the day's hunt, it is no time to count shells when a bird is seen to be coming down crippled. Diving ducks are usually lost if they reach water alive, and river ducks are not necessarily slow about finding places to hide in thick vegetation.

Just ordinary good sense may accomplish a material reduction in game wastage through unretrievable birds. Some marshes, weed growths and river bottomland tangles, on account of dense vegetation, should never be hunted at all for some species of game. Selection of proper shot sizes should not be neglected; mallards can be hit by a large number of 7½ shot and yet remain temporarily functional, while number 2 shot mean wounded birds at nonretrievable distances.

In brief, a great deal of the difference between hunting as the blind and self-destroying shambles that it can be, and the respectable and self-perpetuating sport that it should be, is a matter of headwork on the part of its followers. An understanding of fundamental ecological principles and a willingness to face facts and to modify the practices accordingly should go a long way toward alleviating some of our wildlife crises.

CHAPTER XVII

Estimating the Yearly Production

The initial phase of the Blue-winged Teal research undertaken in 1932 was a study of the nesting habits of the bird. Needless to say, during the nesting season of 1932 several methods of study were used to determine the most efficient duck nest finding technique.

The first system used in looking for nests was that of systematically covering on foot the uncultivated margins of all water areas in the vicinity of Ruthven, Iowa. The margins were a few feet to over one mile in width. A few nests were found, but it soon became apparent that the total number of nests under observation would be very small if one person had to cover 10 or 15 square miles of prospective nesting cover.

Two men stretched a 50 to 75 foot rope tight enough to make it drag easily and at the same time went over the widest strip of ground possible. Several rags were tied to the rope to aid in frightening ducks off of the nests as the rope was dragged over the ground. The method was fairly satisfactory in locating nests. The greatest difficulty with the method was that it was very slow and required an assistant.

Lining up 15 or 20 men and systematically tramping over an area was also used. This method made it possible to locate a high percentage of nests, but of all the methods it was the most unsatisfactory. Fifteen or 20 men walking through a duck nesting area trampled down the vegetation and made paths which were likely to attract predators. When a nest was located it was almost impossible to keep some of the helpers from walking over to the nest to see it, and the result was that the excess trampling became very conspicuous around the nest. Nests found by this method suffered an abnormally high predator loss.

The use of trained dogs proved to be the most successful method of locating nests. Chesapeake, Irish water spaniel and Pointer dogs were used over the five-year period. The Chesapeake and Irish water spaniel were trained to work within 100 yards of the observer and to flush the duck from the nest within sight of the observer. They were also taught neither to chase the bird nor to go near the nest from which the duck flushed. Both varieties of retrievers were excellent aids. The most efficient worker at locating nests was a Pointer dog. Working horizontally with the wind he often covered strips of nesting cover 50 yards wide and 200 yards long on each cast, time after time until the entire area was covered. A remarkably high percentage of nests was found by this dog. The dog rarely flushed a bird from the nest, having been taught to make staunch points 10 to 20 feet from the nest. Many times the ducks would not flush until the observer was past the dog and within a few feet of the nest. In a number of instances the dog pointed nests from which the incubating bird had left a short time before to feed or exercise. Evidently there was enough scent in the nest to attract the dog.

A poorly trained dog was a liability to duck nests and a continual nuisance to the observer. A well-trained dog in the hands of an observer who knows nothing about handling dogs rarely brings about good results. Unless an observer is sure that he has a knack for handling dogs the best methods are rope dragging and search.

DETERMINING THE NESTING POPULATION

Two methods were worked out to determine the yearly nesting populations. Those methods were: *Nest Count Method,* and *Male Count on Waiting Sites.* Each method is described in the following paragraphs.

Nest Count Method. In small areas the combing of all available nesting cover yielded the approximate number of nests. The difficult phase of this method was to determine the percentage of nests not located. The number of nests found depended entirely upon how successful the observer was in his nest finding technique. The author was most successful in locating nests with the assistance of a Pointer dog. The author found that about 75 percent of the duck nests was found by this method. This figure, 75 percent, was arrived at by checking areas such as alfalfa fields and wild hay fields that were to be cut during the middle of the nesting season. The exposed nests were checked against the previous number located by the dog. Thus, when 30 nests on a given area were located by the dog, there were actually about 40 nests on that tract.

Male Count on Waiting Sites. The author found during the course of the duck investigation that the male Blue-winged Teal selected definite waiting sites in a water area where he waited for the female during the nest building and egg-laying period and during the early days of incubation. From May 10 to June 10 the males were counted at their waiting sites to determine the number of nesting birds in a given area. At least 95 percent of the males was found quite easily on the smaller water areas. On the larger water areas about 75 percent of the males was located. The percentage on the larger areas was lower because the males selected muskrat houses in dense growths of bulrushes out in the marsh where they could not be seen. The male counts were checked against the number of nests found and the correlation was found to be very close.

It would be necessary to use the nest count method in carrying on a complete productivity study. The main value of the male count on waiting sites is its value as a supplementary check on the nest count.

DETERMINING THE PERCENTAGE OF YOUNG REACHING THE MIGRATORY STAGE

Each year weekly counts of young with adult females were made from July 1 to August 17. From week to week the average number of young per female indicated the number of young surviving from the date of hatching. The average number of young per female on the last count, August 10-17, indicated the number of young reaching the migratory stage. If the average number of eggs was 9.2 per successful nest and the juvenile count, August 10-17, gave an average of five young per adult female, the survivors would represent 54 percent of the original brood.

DETERMINING THE YEAR'S PRODUCTION

The yearly production of an area may be determined by applying the data obtained on nest densities, nest destruction, successful nests and juvenile survival. The following procedure, if carried out step by step, gives the yearly production.

1. Determine the total number of nests in area.
2. Determine the percentage of successful nests.
3. Multiply the number of successful nests by the average number of eggs in successful nests to determine the number of hatched ducklings.
4. Juvenile counts, August 10-17, indicate the number of young reaching the migratory stage. Multiply the average number of young observed with adult females with the total successful nesting population of females to arrive at the year's production.

The above procedure worked out very well in the Ruthven area. How can the system be applied to an entire breeding area type? Thoeretically the system is feasible over the entire breeding range of the bird. It was found that the shoreline of a marsh had a direct relationship to the nesting area. Ninety-five and six-tenths percent of the Blue-winged Teal nested within 220 yards of the shoreline regardless of the size of the water area. Therefore, the nesting populations may vary several thousand percent between the smallest and the largest water areas. A breeding area type might have 6,000 potholes, 1,200 sloughs and 900 marshes, each group of water areas having vastly different nesting populations. These water areas could be bracketed according to a number of sizes and then by sampling a certain percentage of each bracket at random, the same procedure could be applied as was used in the Ruthven area. Then the findings for each bracket could be multiplied by the total number of water areas in each bracket to determine the year's production in the breeding area type. The author does not contend that the findings in the Ruthven area will apply to all breeding area types. Techniques of study to obtain fundamental data would probably vary greatly in each breeding area type.

CHAPTER XVIII

Future of the Blue-winged Teal

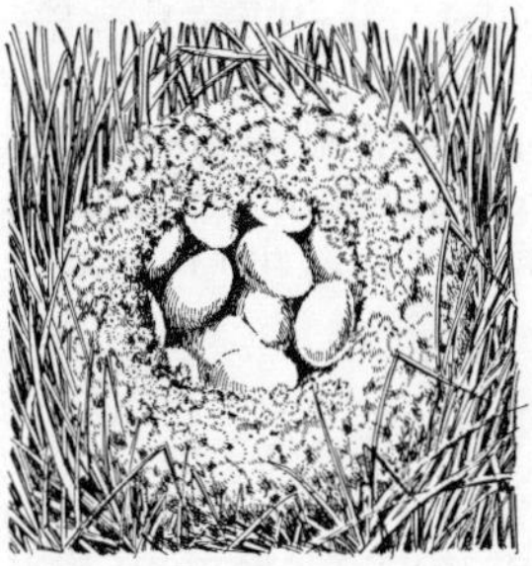

In 1934 and 1935 there were, according to Pearl (1927, p. 14), approximately 125 million people in the United States. Of this number 635,207 hunted ducks in 1934 and 446,822 hunted ducks in 1935; or, 1 person out of every 213 partook of the sport of hunting waterfowl in 1934 and 1 out of 302 in 1935.

RESTORATION OF BREEDING AREAS

Since 1900 about 90 percent of the Blue-winged Teal breeding habitat has been eliminated in the United States by drought, drainage and agriculture. About 50 percent of the breeding range in Canada has been destroyed by the same factors.

The United States Bureau of Biological Survey expanded its migratory waterfowl refuge program in 1934. This expanded program was financed by money derived from the sale of migratory bird hunting stamps and by legislative and executive appropriations. To date, April 1, 1937, thousands of acres of marsh land have been restored within the breeding range of the Blue-winged Teal. The program when initiated had as its objective a long time restoration program of breeding, migratory and wintering refuges (Salyer, 1934). At this time it would be impossible to state what the total acreage of restored breeding areas will be as the years go by.

Many of the states are at the present time restoring and perpetuating marsh lands to furnish breeding habitats for the Blue-winged Teal and other waterfowl.

Throughout the prairie states the lowering of water levels during the past 40 years has prompted a water conservation program for better agriculture. The construction of lakes, ponds and marshes for holding basins for agricultural uses likewise creates breeding grounds for the Blue-winged Teal. Water conservation projects will continue to increase in those semiarid areas, to aid farmers and wildlife. From all indications the period 1930-36 will prove to be the era in which the United States maintained the fewest number of water areas within the breeding range of the Blue-winged Teal.

RAINFALL CYCLES

Meteorologists inform us that the prairie regions have been undergoing a decline in rainfall for a long period of years and that, as far as past records are concerned, in all probability there will eventually begin a long-time upward trend in the rainfall curve. When the upward trend of rainfall begins there will be restored many areas suitable for breeding ducks that private interests and governmental agencies could not afford to rehabilitate.

MIGRATORY REFUGES

The federal and state governments and private organizations have set up refuges along the lines of migratory movement that have been beneficial to the Blue-winged Teal during the spring and fall flights. The shooting areas in the past have out-numbered by far the refuge areas. It is not known as yet what the proper refuge area-shooting area ratio should be. It is certain that the present refuges are inadequate.

WINTERING GROUNDS

The United States has but little control over the Blue-winged Teal on the wintering grounds as at least 95 percent of the birds winters south of the southern boundary. The Blue-winged Teal winters in 16 Republics and numerous possessions of the United States, England, France and other countries. The United States has a migratory bird treaty with one wintering ground country (Mexico, initiated in 1937). It will take years to impress the people of Mexico to abide by the provisions in that treaty. Similar treaties should be made with governments where migratory waterfowl winter, although mere treaties in themselves accomplish little; they are initial attempts in teaching wildlife values.

In countries, such as Mexico, where the Blue-winged Teal is heavily hunted, adequate wintering ground refuges should be established. Such waterfowl management cannot be carried out until more is known about the extent of shooting and concentration areas over the entire wintering range.

HUNTING REGULATIONS

Fortunately for the Blue-winged Teal, during 1934-36, the shooting dates and length of hunting seasons grew progressively better. As the hunting seasons became more restricted sportsmen chose to have the hunting season dates set at such times that bagged birds would be of the larger species. The Blue-winged Teal is one of the earliest fall migrating ducks and in Iowa most of the flight has passed through the state by the last week in October. In 1934 the shooting season opened October 10; in 1935, October 21, and in 1936, November 1. As a result of the late shooting periods in the three zones in 1936 it can be stated that only a few stragglers were killed in the United States.

The Blue-winged Teal will probably be benefited greatly as long as it is necessary to have restricted hunting seasons. At all times the dates of the hunting season should be set to insure the perpetuation and increase of the species.

THE FUTURE

The development of appreciation of our wildlife resources the past few years in the United States seems to lead toward a permanent program for the perpetuation and increase of many of our native wildlife species. Correct land use practices, water conservation, soil conservation and economic evaluation of sporting and nonsporting species have all aided and will continue to better the environment for the Blue-winged Teal. The increase in habitable Blue-winged Teal environment should surpass by several thousand percent the 46 percent increase of hunters by 1960-80. We are passing through the most severe crisis in waterfowl history and the Blue-winged Teal has not been exterminated.

To insure the proper utilization of Blue-winged Teal as a sporting crop the following problems should be attacked and solved:

1. Develop an accurate method of checking yearly production prior to the setting of the shooting season.
2. Set the dates of the shooting season in relation to the yearly surplus.
3. Continue the restoration of breeding areas.
4. Continue the establishment of migratory refuge areas.
5. Carry out migratory bird treaties with countries in which the birds winter.
   a. Determine the yearly kill in wintering grounds.

b. Aid in setting up wintering ground refuges in those countries where there is a need.

6. Continued research on the management of the species in its varied habitats.

THE VALUE OF BLUE-WINGED TEAL ENVIRONMENT TO OTHER SPECIES

This dissertation has dealt almost entirely with the Blue-winged Teal. One of the greatest reasons for the restoration of the bird's habitat is the environment that is provided for other game and nongame species when marshes are restored. In the Ruthven area the following species bred and produced young in the Blue-winged Teal nesting and rearing areas: Eared Grebe *(Colymbus nigricollis californicus)*, Pied-billed Grebe, American Bittern *(Botaurus lentiginosus)*, Eastern Least Bittern *(Ixobrychus exilis exilis)*, Common Mallard, Common Black Duck *(Anas rubripes tristis)*, American Pintail, Shoveller, Redhead, Canvas-back, Ruddy Duck, Marsh Hawk, European Partridge, Eastern Bob-white, Ring-necked Pheasant, King Rail, Virginia Rail *(Rallus limicola limicola)*, Sora *(Porzana carolina)*, Florida Gallinule *(Gallinula chloropus cachinnans)*, American Coot *(Fulica americana americana)*, Killdeer *(Oxyechus vociferus vociferus)*, Upland Plover *(Bartramia longicauda)*, Spotted Sandpiper *(Actitis macularia)*, Eastern Solitary Sandpiper *(Tringa solitaria solitaria)*, Wilson's Phalarope *(Steganopus tricolor)*, Forster's Tern*(Sterna forsteri)*, Black Tern *(Chlidonias nigra surinamensis)*, Western Burrowing Owl *(Speotyto cunicularia hypugaea)*, Short-eared Owl *(Asio flammeus flammeus)*, Eastern Belted Kingfisher *(Megaceryle alcyon alcyon)*, Prairie Horned Lark *(Otocoris alpestris praticola)*, Prairie Marsh Wren *(Telmatodytes palustris dissaeptus)*, Short-billed Marsh Wren *(Cistothorus stellaris)*, Northern Yellow-throat *(Geohlypis trichas brachidactyla)*, Bobolink *(Dolichonyx oryzivorus)*, Western Meadowlark *(Sturnella neglecta)*, Giant Red-wing *(Agelaius phoeniceus arctolegus)*, Eastern Cowbird *(Molothrus ater ater)*, Dickcissel *(Spiza americana)*, Western Grasshopper Sparrow *(Ammodramus savannarum bimaculatus)*, Leconte's Sparrow *(Passerherbulus caudacutus)*, Nelson's Sparrow *(Ammospiza caudacuta nelsoni)*, Western Henslow's Sparrow *(Passerherbulus henslowi henslowi)*, and muskrat, mink, striped skunk, American badger, Mearns' cottontail *(Sylvilagus floridanus mearnsi)*, white-tailed jack rabbit *(Lepus townsendii campanius)*, coyote and red fox.

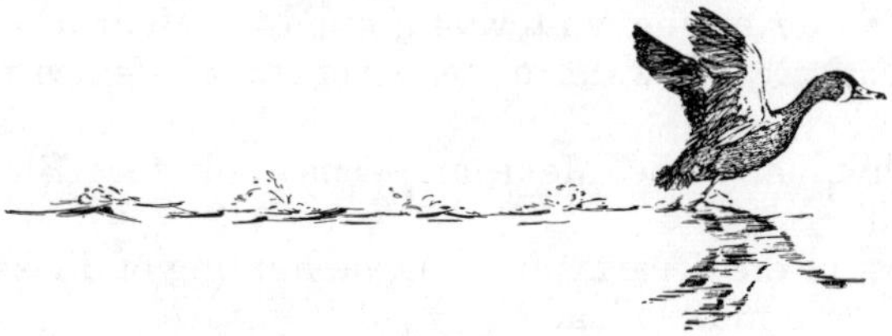

CHAPTER XIX

Summary and Conclusions

1. Approximately 20 per cent of the Blue-winged Teal is produced in the United States.
2. Eighty percent is produced in Canada.
3. About 30 percent of the Blue-winged Teal breeding range is suitable for their propagation at present.
4. The main breeding area types are: The true Prairie Area; Mixed Prairie; Boreal Forest Area, Deciduous Forest Area and the Lake Forest Area.
5. The fall migration begins the last two weeks in August.
6. The major portion of the fall flight is down the Mississippi Valley and Central Flyways.
7. Most of the fall flight movement takes place early in the morning and late in the evening.
8. Drought conditions concentrate the birds during migration.
9. The daily length of flight on a straight line course averages up to 85 miles or more.
10. Most of the birds migrate at a speed of 30 to 40 miles per hour.
11. Migrating birds were usually observed at heights less than 3,000 feet.
12. Blue-winged Teal were observed associating with many species of waterfowl during the fall flight.
13. Migrating flocks were usually composed of less than 30 birds.
14. There was no food shortage in the Iowa marshes.
15. At least 95 percent of the Blue-winged Teal winters south of the United States.

16. The birds were observed only on fresh water and brackish water on the wintering grounds in Mexico.
17. Practically all water areas observed in Mexico were shot over.
18. Individually the Mexican peons took few Blue-winged Teal.
19. Most of the firearms used in the hunting of ducks in Mexico were muzzle loaders.
20. Blue-winged Teal were sold in the markets of Mexico.
21. Spring migration began in January on the wintering grounds.
22. Courtship began on the wintering grounds and was closely associated with the spring migration.
23. The male birds began to acquire their nuptial plumage in December on the wintering grounds. By the time the birds reached Iowa at the end of March all the birds had acquired the breeding plumage.
24. Courtship became more ardent as the birds neared the breeding grounds.
25. There was much courting by both sexes.
26. The most ardent of the courting occurred on the water and along the beaches.
27. Pairs became definitely mated.
28. Copulation took place on the water.
29. Blue-winged Teal were noncombative with other species.
30. Both male and female selected the home base water area.
31. The female selected the nesting site.
32. The nest was built in a scooped out hollow in the soil or rotten vegetation.
33. The nest was constructed of grasses or sedges and lined with down.
34. The nests were 7 to 10 inches in diameter and 4 to 6 inches in depth.
35. Down feathers were added to the nest each day until the young hatched.
36. The average number of eggs per nest was 9.3.
37. Renesting attempt nests contained an average of 4.3 eggs.
38. Male birds selected waiting sites while the females built the nests and deposited eggs.
39. Male birds deserted the females shortly after incubation began.
40. Many eggs were dropped promiscuously early in the nesting season before nests were constructed.

41. The average distance of nests from water was 41.5 yards. The extremes were: nests in water and two nests one mile from water.
42. After egg laying in the nests began, one egg was deposited each day until the clutch was completed.
43. Incubation began within 24 hours after the last egg had been laid.
44. The ducklings hatched 21 to 23 days after incubation began.
45. After incubation began the female bird almost invariably defecated on the eggs when flushed.
46. Injury feigning on the part of the female increased with advanced incubation.
47. The nesting territory was that margin of land within 220 yards of the water area. Ninety-five and six-tenths percent of the nests was found within the 220-yard margin.
48. There were no territorial disputes by either males or females.
49. Of 223 initial nesting attempts, 59.6 percent was successful.
50. Of 27 renesting attempts, 14.8 percent was successful.
51. The young ducklings walked to water within 12 hours after hatching.
52. Nest losses were attributed to mowing, flooding, trampling by cattle, desertion, infertility of eggs, burning, unknown causes, crows, striped skunk, Franklin's ground squirrel, mink, badger and unknown mammals.
53. Drought and overgrazing were detrimental to breeding grounds.
54. Ring-necked Pheasants parasitized 4.7 percent of the duck nests from 1933 to 1935.
55. The pheasant parasitized duck nests contained fewer duck eggs than normal duck nests.
56. The prairie region supported a moderate population of predators.
57. There were no epidemics of parasites or diseases in the study area.
58. Each pair of Blue-winged Teal under observation that stopped to nest in Iowa apparently started south the following fall (1932-36) with 3.09 young ducks.
59. There were three common types of nesting cover in Iowa: bluegrass, slough grass and alfalfa.
60. The bluegrass cover was 12-16 inches high, the slough

grass 30-40 inches high, and the alfalfa 14-16 inches high at the close of the nesting season.

61. The common types of rearing cover were: great bulrush, round bulrush and river bulrush associes; river bulrush, great bulrush and bur-reed associes; river bulrush and cat-tail associes; river bulrush and sedge associes; reed and cat-tail associes; bur-reed, sweet flag and larger blue flag associes.
62. The food items eaten by Blue-winged Teal consisted of over 125 species of plants (chiefly plants in families, Cyperaceae, Najadaceae, Gramineae and Polygonaceae) and about 100 species of animals (chiefly insects and molluscs).
63. The sex ratio of the Blue-winged Teal was 1 female to 1.5 males.
64. The heaviest males were noted on the wintering grounds. The heaviest females were collected just prior to the nesting season. The lightest males were collected during the spring and summer. The lightest females were collected during the rearing season.
65. Drainage of 6,000,000 acres of waterfowl habitat in Iowa has been very successful from an agricultural standpoint. About 5 percent of the drainage has not been successful.
66. Overgrazing eliminated nesting possibilities. The effects of overgrazing were detrimental to the pastures from a grazing and from a duck nesting standpoint.
67. Capacity grazed areas supported one nest per 20 acres.
68. Lightly grazed areas supported one nest per 9.3 acres.
69. Areas protected from all grazing supported one nest per 11 acres.
70. The proper utilization of many marshes and marsh margins was conducive to the production of the Blue-winged Teal.
71. The prairie habitat was the most desirable Blue-winged Teal breeding environment.
72. No Blue-winged Teal nests were found in or under shrubs or trees.
73. Trees and shrubs crowded out desirable nesting cover.
74. Trees in the nesting regions harbored crows and Great Horned Owls.
75. The shoreline length of a marsh had a direct relationship to the nesting area. The longer the shoreline in proportion to the water area the greater the acreage of usable nesting territory.

76. The proper manipulation of water levels in the Iowa marshes proved to be the key for providing adequate food and rearing cover.
77. Crippling losses equaled 26 percent of the number of birds actually shot.
78. Crowded shooting led to poor shooting and increased cripple losses.
79. All Blue-winged Teal duck hunters should use retrieving dogs to obtain fallen birds.
80. More shooting areas are needed to eliminate crowded hunting conditions.
81. More refuges are needed. The proportion of refuges to shooting areas is at present in some parts of the state too low.
82. The proper use of land, water conservation, restoration of water areas by federal and state governments, and private organizations will in all likelihood insure a permanent breeding habitat for the Blue-winged Teal.
83. More favorable climatic conditions would favor the Blue-winged Teal as well as agriculture.
84. Further research is needed on the ecology and management of the Blue-winged Teal in its varied habitats.

LITERATURE CITED

American Ornithologists' Union
1931. Check-list of North American Birds. Fourth Edition, Published by American Ornithologists' Union.

Bailey, Florence Merriam
1928. Birds of New Mexico. Judd and Detweiler, Inc., Washington, D. C.

Bangs, Outram
1907. On a Collection of Birds from Western Costa Rico. The Auk, 24: 287-312.

Barbour, Thomas
1923. The Birds of Cuba. Mem. Nuttall Orn. Club, No. 6, Cambridge, Massachusetts.

Bell, W. B.
1934. Status of Waterfowl in 1934. U. S. Dept. of Agri., Miscellaneous Publication 210.

Bennett, Logan J.
1932. A Preliminary Study of the Ecology of the Native Wild Ducks of Iowa. Unpublished Master's degree thesis, Iowa State College.

Bennett, Logan J.
1933. Nineteen Thirty-two Fall Flight of Ducks in Northwestern Iowa. Wilson Bulletin, 45: 85-86.

BENNETT, LOGAN J.
1936. The Ring-necked Pheasant as a Nesting Parasite of Other Game Birds. Iowa State College Journal of Science, 10:373-375.

BENNETT, LOGAN J.
1936. Duck Nesting Carrying Capacities in Iowa. North American Wildlife Conference. Wildlife Restoration and Conservation. pp. 494-498. U. S. Govt. Print. Off.

BENT, A. C.
1923. Life Histories of North American Wildfowl. U. S. National Museum, Bulletin 126.

BERLEPSCH, HANS VON
1908. Original not seen. Cited in Phillips, 1923, p. 378.

BOND, JAMES
1936. The Birds of the West Indies. The Academy of Natural Sciences of Philadelphia.

BRADLEE, T. S., L. L. MAWBRAY AND W. F. EATON
1931. A List of Birds Recorded From Bermuda. Proc. Boston Soc. Nat. Hist., 39:279-382.

CHAPMAN, FRANK M.
1917. The Distribution of Bird-Life in Colombia. American Museum of Natural History, Bulletin 36.

CHAPMAN, FRANK M.
1926. The Distribution of Bird-Life in Ecuador. American Museum of Natural Hisotry, Bulletin 55.

CHAPMAN, FRANK M.
1894. On the Birds of the Island of Trinidad. American Museum of Natural History, Bulletin 6.

CHUBB, CHARLES
1916. Birds of British Guiana. B. Quaritch, London.

COOKE, W. W.
1884. Bird Nomenclature of the Chippewa Indians. The Auk, 1:242-250.

COOKE, W. W.
1906. Distribution and Migration of North American Ducks, Geese and Swans. U. S. Bureau of Biological Survey, Bulletin 26.

CORY, CHARLES B.
1888. The Birds of the West Indies, Including the Bahama Islands, the Greater and Lesser Antilles, Excepting the Islands of Tobago and Trinidad. The Auk, 5:48-82.

CORY, CHARLES B.
1890. The Birds of the Bahama Islands. Estes and Lauriat. Boston.

DANFORTH, STUART T.
1936. Personal correspondence. November 11.

DAWSON, WILLIAM LEON
1932. The Birds of California. South Moulton Company, Los Angeles.

ELWELL, AMBROSE J., AND J. L. BOATMAN
1923. Soil Survey of Dickinson County, Iowa. U. S. Department of Agriculture.

ERRINGTON, PAUL L.
1936. Food Habits of a Weasel Family. Journal of Mammalogy, 17:406-407.

ERRINGTON, PAUL L
1937. Summer Food Habits of the Badger in Northwest Iowa. (In Press.)

ERRINGTON, PAUL L., AND LOGAN J. BENNETT
1933. Lost Legions. Outdoor Life, 72, 3:18-19, 56.

ERRINGTON, PAUL L., AND LOGAN J. BENNETT
1933. Mid-West Duck Breeding Grounds. Minnesota Conservationist, 7, 4:8, 18-20.

ERRINGTON, PAUL L., AND LOGAN J. BENNETT
1934. Iowa Duck Studies. Transactions, 20th American Game Conference, Washington.

ERRINGTON, PAUL L., AND W. J. BRECKENRIDGE
1936. Food Habits of Marsh Hawks in the Glaciated Region of North-central United States. The American Midland Naturalist, 7:831-848

FEILDEN, HENRY W.
1889. On the Birds of Barbados. The Ibis, 6, 4:477-503.

FISHER, A. K.
1893. Report on the ornithology of the Death Valley Expedition of 1891, comprising notes on the birds observed in Southern California, Southern Nevada, and parts of Arizona and Utah. U. S Bureau of Biological Survey, North American Fauna 7, Part 2.

FURNISS, O. C.
1935. The Sex Ratio in Ducks. Wilson Bulletin, 47:277-278.

GOSSE, PHILLIP HENRY
1847. Birds of Jamaica. John Van Voorst, London.

GRAY, ASA
1908. New Manual of Botany, 7th edition. American Book Company, New York.

HICKS, LAWRENCE E.
1935. Distribution of Breeding Birds of Ohio. Ohio State University Studies, 40.

HOWELL, ARTHUR H.
1911. Birds of Arkansas. U. S. Bureau of Biological Survey, Bulletin 38.

HOWELL, ARTHUR H.
1932. Florida Bird Life. Florida Dept. of Game and Fresh Water Fish.

KALMBACH, E. R.
1934. Western Duck Sickness: A Form of Botulism. U. S. Department of Agriculture, Technical Bulletin 411.

KENNARD, FRED H.
1919. Q. d. albinucha subsp. n. The Auk, 36: 455-465.

LEOPOLD, ALDO
1933. Game Management. Charles Scribner's Sons, New York.

LINCOLN, FREDERICK C.
1935. The Migration of North American Birds. U. S. Department of Agriculture, Circular No. 363.

LINCOLN, FREDERICK C.
1936. Returns of Banded Birds. Bird-banding, 7: 121-128.

LOUISIANA DEPARTMENT OF CONSERVATION
1931. The Birds of Louisiana. Louisiana Department of Conservation.

MCATEE, W. L.
1923. Local Names of Migratory Game Birds. U. S. Department of Agriculture, Miscellaneous Circular 13.

MABBOTT, DOUGLAS C.
1920. Food Habits of Seven Shoal-water Ducks. U. S. Department of Agriculture, Bulletin 862.

MURPHY, ROBERT CUSHMAN
1936. Oceanic Birds of South America. American Museum of Natural History.

NAUMBURG, ELSIE M. B.
1926. The Bird Fauna of North America in Relation to Its Distribution in South America. The Auk, 43: 485-492.

OBERHOLSER, HARRY C.
1921. Sixth Annual List of Proposed Changes in the A. O. U. Check-list of North American Birds. The Auk, 38: 264-269.

O'ROKE, EARL C.
1934. A Malaria-like Disease of Ducks. University of Michigan, School of Forestry and Conservation, Bulletin 4.

OSGOOD, W. H., AND BOARDMAN CONOVER
1922. Game Birds from Northwestern Venezuela. Field Museum of Natural History. Zoological Series, 12, 3: 19-47.

PEARL, RAYMOND
1927. The Biology of Population Growth. Alfred A. Knopf, Inc., New York.

PENARD, E. F., AND A. P. PENARD
1908-10. De Vogels von Guayana. Paramaribo.

PHILLIPS, JOHN C.
1923. A Natural History of the Ducks. Vol. 2. Houghton Mifflin Company.

PHILLIPS, JOHN C., AND FREDERICK C. LINCOLN
1930. American Waterfowl. Houghton Mifflin Company.

PRATT, HENRY SHERRING
1935. Vertebrate Animals of the United States. P. Blakiston's Son & Co., Inc., Philadelphia.

PREBLE, EDWARD A.
1902. A Biological Investigation of the Hudson Bay Region. U .S. Bureau of Biological Survey. North American Fauna 22.

PREBLE,, EDWARD A.
1908. A Biological Investigation of the Athabaska-Mackenzie Region. U. S. Bureau of Biological Survey. North American Fauna 27.

REID, S. G.
1884. The Birds of Bermuda. U. S. National Museum, Bulletin 25.

SALYER, J. CLARK II
1934. A Program of Waterfowl Restoration. U. S. Department of Agriculture, Circular 339.

SCHALOW, HERMAN
1898. Die Vögel der Sammlung Plate. Zool. Jahrb., Supplementband. 4:641-749. (Fauna Chilensis, V. 1.)

SCOTT, W. E. D.
1891. Observations on the Birds of Jamaica, West Indies. The Auk, 8:353-365.

SOOTER, CLARENCE
1937. Leeches Infesting Young Waterfowl in Northwest Iowa. The Journal of Parasitology, 23:108-109..

STODDARD, HERBERT L.
1931. The Bob-white Quail: Its Habits, Preservation and Increase. Charles Scribner's Sons, New York.

STURGIS, BERTHA B.
1928. Field Book of Birds of the Panama Canal Zone. C. P. Putnam's Sons, New York.

SWARTH, H. S.
1915. An Apparent Hybrid Between Species of the Genera Spatula and Querquedula. The Condor, 17:115-118.

TAVERNER, P. A.
1934. Birds of Canada. Canada Geological Survey, National Museum of Canada, Bulletin 72.

THOMPSON, ERNEST EVAN
1890. The Birds of Manitoba. Proceedings U. S. National Museum, 13:457-643.

WELLS, JOHN GRANT
1902. Birds of the Island af Carriacou. The Auk, 19:237-246.

WETMORE, ALEXANDER
1916. Birds of Porto Rico. U. S. Department of Agriculture, Bulletin 326.

WETMORE, ALEXANDER, AND BRADSHAW H. SWALES
1931. The Birds of Haiti and the Dominican Republic. U. S. National Museum, Bulletin 155.

Index